About the Author.

Having completed a Psychology degree, Rukshana had a passion for travel and writing. She worked for an airline for twenty-five years, (of course, she started when she was three!) and combined her two passions by travelling and writing about her travels. As this is her first novel, she is nervous about it and while she wanted to get it published, she doesn't want anyone to read it!

She has delivered a baby at thirty-five thousand feet, trained the most challenging flight and cabin crew and coached frustrated CEOs but says all of that combined, does not compare to the challenge of bringing up her daughter, (now fourteen years old).

Life on a Postcard

Rukshana Chenoy-Horwood

Life on a Postcard

Olympia Publishers
London

www.olympiapublishers.com
OLYMPIA PAPERBACK EDITION

A CIP catalogue record for this title is available from the British Library.

ISBN: 978-1-78830-986-8

This is a work of fiction.
Names, characters, places and incidents originate from the writer's imagination. Any resemblance to actual persons, living or dead, is purely coincidental.

First Published in 2022

Olympia Publishers
Tallis House
2 Tallis Street
London
EC4Y 0AB

Printed in Great Britain

Dedication.

This book is dedicated to my mum.
You are the inspiration for this book,
I love you more than my hair straighteners,
You are and always will be, the wind beneath my wings.

And to my daughter, Lilya, who I love almost as much as my
travel coffee mug — who will hopefully read this book and
laugh

Acknowledgements.

Porus Munshi — Without you, this book would never have been published. Your unwavering belief in me, that this was a good book and was worth others reading, is one of the main reasons it is now in print. You persevered for me even when I stopped trying. The support and help you gave me and the time and effort you put into this, has been unbelievable.

Thank you hardly seems enough.

Asmita Marwa — Personally over the last couple of years, you have been there for me constantly and consistently during some of the most challenging times. You have encouraged and supported me throughout this process. You continue to support, encourage and especially help me in aspects of this new adventure that I am not familiar with.

When I am with you, I'm standing with an army.

Story of my life.

Life on a Postcard is just that — my life on a postcard. Well, several postcards.

The story is told through many snap shots, anecdotes and incidents. It follows the life of a young girl, as speedily as paparazzi photographing a minor female celebrity's crotch, as she gets out of her hired car when she has 'accidentally on purpose' forgotten to wear her knickers.

The young girl is plucked from her very comfortable existence in Middle England, in the middle of her fourteenth year and transported to... where else? Hyderabad, India of course. Here she experiences the local culture, local neighbours, local hospitals and local boys.

She then returns to England where she joins an airline, travels the world and has many adventures.

There are more twists and turns and strange happenings in this book than you can shake a (middle-class), organic, free-range egg at.

It's a hilarious combination of real-life scenarios, embellished with a huge side-order of poetic licence, a dollop of 'out of the box' imagination and pure fiction. And yes, the reader can be forgiven for sometimes thinking I am on the hard stuff — sugar-coated doughnuts, topped with fruit pastilles.

They say you should 'write what you know'. I wouldn't know how to write anything else.

This is the story of my life... well, almost my life... well, fifty per cent of it. Okay... a lot of it is made up.

Preface.
Nothing to Write Home About.

So, why did I write this book? Because I was afraid.

1. Afraid I would eventually lose my sense of humour, so I wanted to capture it before it was gone.

2. Afraid that I might combust internally if I didn't put on paper, all the stuff that was in my head.

3. And afraid to be a stand-up comedian so I hid behind this book.

Stand-up comedians, in my opinion, are some of the bravest people in the world. Of course, you have your firefighters, soldiers and policemen, etc. and lots of other brave people. Yes, I will also mention parking attendants. What do you mean, 'Are you crazy?' They *are* brave, as there is a real danger of them being killed, stabbed or at least maimed, each time they go to work — perhaps with good reason, but it still takes bravery and courage to know you are hated for what you do.

But I digress. Where was I? Oh yes, stand-up comedians. Yes, I think they are hugely brave. Not in the categories I have already mentioned, but standing in front of an audience who is looking at them thinking, 'Go on, make me laugh', strips them of everything that they want to protect about themselves — dignity, control, pride. They stand up there not knowing which way the wind will blow.

I was too afraid to do that. So, ladies and gentlemen, here is my stand-up routine in the written word.

However, what purpose this story will have, I don't know. If it even helps one person to take heed or makes the reader sit up and think, I will puke. My reason for writing it is purely to entertain and if it does any more than that, then I apologise profusely from the start. If it does any less than that, then may it die an unnatural death or worse, be banished to the shelves of a Charity Shop; a fate worse than death for a book.

All the characters in this book are purely fictional (yeah, right!) and any resemblance to any person dead or alive is pure coincidence. (Hopefully, that will get me out of any law suits.)

Postcard No. 30
And the Breasts Got in The Way

Dear Mother,

I didn't think medical emergencies could get worse than having to deliver a baby at thirty-five thousand feet and injecting an eighteen-year-old in the heart. Once I had done that, I was ready for anything. They could throw anything at me and I would be ready for it. What could possibly be more challenging than that?

Well, for starters...

We were over the Atlantic, about an hour away from Atlanta in the US. The captain had just put on the seatbelt signs as there was some 'clear air turbulence' ahead. Don't ask me what that means. I'm not sure whether the opposite would be polluted air turbulence or cloudy air turbulence. However, we started to check the passengers and I was just passing the mid-galley, when we hit a huge pocket of air and dropped about fifty feet in one fell swoop. No pun there at all. That is what it was like: a swoop.

Some of the canisters fell out of their stowage's above the seats and one hit a colleague on the head and he literally passed out in front of me. I ran to help him but one of the other crew got to him first and started to administer first aid. I ran into the cabin to see if anyone else was hurt and started checking the passengers; all had their seat belts on.

The plane was now shaking from side to side like a giant had got hold of the aluminium tube and was shaking it, trying to get the last drop of his favourite drink out. The overhead lockers were opening with the violent rattling and bags were falling out everywhere.

As I went down the aisle, a gentleman grabbed me and pointed to the passenger next to him. She was either asleep — highly unlikely as the turbulence was enough to wake the dead... poor choice of thought really — or she had passed out. I looked around to see if anything had hit her on the head or if she had any head injuries. The passenger assured me nothing had struck her. She had passed out the moment the turbulence started but before passing out, she had been clutching her chest and trying to take her clothes off, as if they were restricting her.

I shouted to one of my colleagues, "Get the Defib. I think she's had a heart attack."

"You're kidding me!" my colleague shouted, as he tried to put some of the baggage back into the overhead lockers and reassure the passengers at the same time.

"I wish I was," I shouted back.

I asked the male passenger to help me and together we placed the lady in the aisle. I was just about to commence CPR on her when the aircraft, which had now been shuddering at an even pace (and I had got used to the rhythm of the turbulence), suddenly dropped another fifty feet, sending the lady and me a few rows down the aisle towards the galley. Finally, when we came to a stop, I started CPR.

I gave her a few puffs and then started the chest compressions. I tried to rip off her blouse, which was a front-buttoned one. Have you ever tried to rip off a front-buttoned blouse? Not just ripping it off but doing that in heavy turbulence? Well, I can tell you, it's not like you see in the movies, where the buttons fly and pop everywhere with one yank. I yanked and yanked and it would not rip off. Finally, I thought it would be quicker to unbutton it one button at a time. However, before I could start doing that, the defibrillator was thankfully by my side.

The kit always had a pair of scissors for this very occasion. I got them out and made sure I steadied myself with one hand, while another crew member held me steady,

I cut carefully through her blouse and was dismayed at the sight that met my eyes: she had the largest boobs I had ever seen.

Talk about 'Over-the-shoulder-boulder-holders' — it was going to take me a month to cut through her bra.

Luckily, it seemed to have a weak point as I cut through the bit in the middle of the cups. As I did so, her breasts fell out and I really did feel like Harrison Ford in one of those *Indiana Jones* movies — each time I overcame one task or challenge, I was faced with another. I was just trying to decide where to place the defib and whether her bust would inhibit the contact, when they both flopped to either side of her and lay neatly under each arm. For the first time in my life I shouted, "Thank god for saggy boobs!"

These are not the kind of obstacles they tell you about in the training school. Oh no, they don't warn you about large boobs or cutting bras.

I finally managed to get the defib in the right place and my colleague and I worked in tandem: CPR, mouth to mouth, chest compressions, defib. But she was flat lined. We couldn't see any fibrillation. No vital signs. Nothing.

She wasn't travelling with anyone, so we couldn't get any further information. One of our colleagues had gone through her handbag to see if she had any preconditions or anything that would help us.

After forty minutes, we were exhausted. The turbulence had passed but neither of us were ready to let her go. Two of our other colleagues were getting ready to take over when suddenly, we saw a flicker. We kept going till suddenly, she threw up all over us.

She coughed and spluttered everywhere. We turned her onto her side, gently removed all the debris from her mouth and put her in the recovery position, then rose from our positions covered in vomit and drool. But as we rose up to our feet, we were met with the loudest applause I had ever heard.

Passengers were standing in their seats and on their seats, clapping as we walked down the aisle smelling of sick and about to throw up ourselves.

But that didn't detract from the feeling of complete euphoria.

At that moment, I was almost grateful at the way my life had turned out.

And there ended one of my many postcards to Mother.

How exactly did I get here? How exactly did I end up cutting the bra straps of a big-busted woman and saving her life?

I thought you would never ask!

Postcard No. 8
Time for A Flashback

I was in my fourteenth year. In a few moments, I will implore you to travel with me through some snapshots of my previous years. Stay with me through the good times, cry with me through the pain, be scared for me through the scary times and accompany me on this roller coaster ride of emotions that is my life. But first, I ask you to hold hands with me in my fourteenth year, as this one was more significant than all the others. The journey I am about to take you on and the bombshell I am about to drop on you, will bring out the range of emotions I have just described.

Dad worked for the Government. What he did, where he worked and how he did it, was a mystery to everyone.

'I can't really say', was his stock answer each time anyone asked him anything about his work, much like our MPs today. That's it! He must have been an MP!

But I digress. Here it comes. One Sunday, which was like any other Sunday, except that it wasn't, Dad was talking about how wonderful it was to travel and that travel was the best education a person could have. Mum and I nodded as we usually did, while thinking about various other things.

Then Dad said, "We haven't had much of a summer this year. I'm sure other parts of the world are having lovely weather now."

Again, robotic nodding from the two of us. Please don't feel sorry for Dad, he was used to this.

He carried on regardless, then turning to Mum, he said, "What do you think the weather is like in India this time of the year, darling?"

Mother absentmindedly, half-heartedly, with a sideways glance, as she was flicked a spot of casserole off the tablecloth, said, "Hmmmmmm, well dear, I presume it must be lovely."

To which Dad replied, "Good, because we're moving there next month."

I was still thinking of my 'various things' but vaguely became aware that Mum had stopped thinking about her 'various things' and seemed to be paying attention to what Dad was saying.

Mum smirked and said, "Sorry, darling? I think I misheard you. Who's moving where, did you say?" She took a gulp from her water glass.

"We are moving to India," Dad said, "sometime next month."

Hindsight, they say, is a wonderful thing and in this case, I do believe it was up to Dad to have stopped her taking that gulp *before* repeating his sentence and therefore he deserved what he got, which was an eyeful of water that shot out from my Mum's mouth, at a speed that would have put any of Nadal's serves to shame.

By this time, I realised this was not our usual Sunday lunch conversation and wanted to be part of it. Thus, I asked Dad to repeat what he had said, which had made Mum do her impression of the young girl possessed in *The Exorcist*.

Dad wiped his eyes calmly, though I could see he had been nearly blinded by the speed with which the water had hit him and he repeated his sentence again.

When I finally realised what he was saying, I gave a

performance to rival any renowned Shakespearean actor. I cried, "Why? Why? Why?" several times. I threw my hands up in the air. I convulsed on the floor. I feigned having a heart attack. And finally, I asked him why he had bothered to bring me into this world just to ruin my life.

"Now now. Could everyone calm down just a *little*," Dad said. "We are not moving to Jupiter; we are moving to one of the most exotic and culturally vibrant places in the world."

Much handwringing from Mum ensued. However, I chose to throw mine up in the air several times, as that was far more dramatic.

Finally, Mum was the first one to decide it was time to move on and accept that maybe Dad wasn't joking.

"Where in India are you proposing to take us?"

"Hyderabad."

"Hamalamabad?" said Aunt Sybil, when we told her. "Never heard of it."

Aunt Sybil was Dad's sister and you could always count on her to get it wrong. When her daughter, Cousin Alicia, got married she decided it would be prudent to take two hankies, in case she cried excessively and tucked them into her blouse.

During the service, she was boo-hooing all over the place and having found one of the hankies, started to look for the other around her chest area. When she couldn't find it, she said in a loud voice, while still feeling her bosoms, "I'm sure I had two when I left home."

As this was caught on video, she has never been allowed to forget it.

Aunt Sybil had 'married well' and her husband, Uncle Robert, not only had inherited wealth but an uncanny knack of making more as well. Cousin Alicia had married a wank—

sorry, a banker, who was equally wealthy. This was just as well as Cousin Alicia had not only been born with a silver spoon in her mouth but had been born with a diamond-encrusted, gold, spoon in her mouth. You will hear more about her later. Now, where was I...? oh yes, we were leaving...

Over the next month, many a tear was shed and many goodbyes were exchanged. Sympathetic sounds were heard from Mother's friends and numerous conversations were had, on whether there was any way out of this. It was even suggested Mum got pregnant again. But even she could not perform such a miracle: I was her first and last.

When it had been decided that there wasn't any way out, hundreds of suggestions were given as to what to take with us, what to do, what not to do and above all, 'do not drink any of the water', we were told.

"And what do you propose we do when we are thirsty?" asked Dad.

"Drink wine," we were advised.

All options had now been exhausted and we were going. Bags were packed — or I should say, *filled*; 'packed' would be too orderly a word for it. The only saving grace for Mum and me was that we were allowed, within reason, to take whatever we thought we would need from home. This included my dressing table and all of Mum's bedding but Dad drew the line at my Mum's potted plants, assuring her that flora and fauna were both commonly found all over India.

Postcard No. 9
Safe Landings: Meeting the Locals

We arrived in Hyderabad weary from the journey but wide-eyed with expectation, terribly tired, but excited... also, a bit sad and apprehensive but enthusiastic. We really didn't know how we were feeling.

We were told we had been allocated a car and driver and we would be picked up from the airport. As we waited outside, a car drove up and the driver waved to us so vigorously we thought his wrist would snap. He stopped the car right in front of us and jumped out. There, standing in front of us, was the smallest man we had ever seen. He was perfectly formed with the most gorgeous smile. We all looked at him quite surprised and then in unison, moved our gaze towards the car. He nodded as if he understood every word we had not spoken. "It is adapted for me, sir. All my life I have wanted to be a driver. My dream came true with the help of God and the nice people at the Ambassador factory. Come, we must go." We soon came to realise this was Daniel's favourite sentence and he always laughed each time he used it. He loved the 'irony of the opposites', as he used to call them.

Daniel was from the Anglo-Indian community in India. During the time Britain ruled India, children born legitimately and illegitimately to British men and Indian women, had been treated as outcasts and began to form their own community. They then married each other and had children of their own, hence the Anglo-Indian community was born (no pun intended). Some looked white and you could not tell them apart from Caucasians and some were darker and looked very much Indian.

Daniel drove like a Rottweiler on heat, but I guess with the Indian traffic, one had to. However, Daniel drove like that even when there was no traffic.

We arrived forty-five minutes later at what was to be our home for the next few years. We had to virtually prise our fingers out of the backs of the seats in front of us, where they had been embedded for most of our journey. We then had to extricate our legs from the imaginary brake pedals we had been pressing throughout our hair-raising ride. The *Double Dipper* at Thorpe Park was not a patch on Daniel's driving.

We had been provided with the most beautiful bungalow with a huge veranda, that had been sculpted around the whole house — your typical, white, colonial house.

Waiting to greet us were:

1. Cook, who had the roughest hands we had ever felt but the kindest face.

2. Maid, who was so neat she almost had her saree wrapped around her with the precision of hospital bed corners.

3. Nanny, who had a face like a robber's dog but who was caring, strict and efficient.

Mum said if it hadn't been for the heat, the dust, the different language, the food and the accents she couldn't understand, it would have been heaven on earth. She had never really had the stomach for travel to 'foreign lands'. Dad and I took to it like dogs to mud but Mum never really fitted in. While Dad and I learnt the languages, Mum persevered and tried to teach everyone English. Dad and I got used to the food and Mum desperately tried to teach Cook how to make bread and butter pudding and roast dinners. She never learnt her lesson even when Cook, who refused to prepare a dish without salt or chilli, included some in her Yorkshire puds. Mum screamed blue murder, but Cook said, "Madam, how you can eat, madam! No taste, madam, without chilli." Mum still never gave up.

Dad and I treated our car journeys with Daniel as free fun-fair rides, whereas Mum became addicted to Valium, after taking one each time she sat in the car.

Dan drove like he was trying to take off each time and joked that Mum's two favourite Hindi words were 'no' (*nahi*) and 'slower' (*asthe*). In fact, they were Mum's *only* two Hindi words.

Hyderabad was the most fascinating place we had ever heard of or been to. It was a dusty, dirty, overcrowded, chaotic city but the people were hospitable and friendly. The streets were full of traffic. I counted eleven modes of traffic: cars, lorries, buses, scooters, motorbikes with sidecars, bicycles, auto rickshaws, cycle rickshaws, pedestrians, bullock carts and most importantly, cows. Holy cows! They sat in the middle of the roads, oblivious to the traffic struggling to get around them. As cows are sacred in India, no one could move them. If they wanted to sit in the middle of the road then we, as motorists, needed to accommodate them.

What struck me the most, were the colours we saw everywhere. The festivals were full of colour, the clothes were full of colour and the language was full of colour — there are twenty-two official languages in India and seven hundred and twenty dialects. Holi was the Festival of Colour, when people literally threw colour on each other! It didn't get more colourful than that. Diwali, the Festival of Lights, lit up the whole city with *diyas*, candles and colourful lights. What is irrefutable is that the Indian people are the most hospitable, friendliest and most helpful people I have ever come across.

India was also a country of extremes. There was abject poverty and eye-watering wealth and riches, sometimes within spitting distance of each other.

There were beggars everywhere and we couldn't go into the High Street without been plagued by beggars. If we gave one a rupee, we would not be allowed to move on till we had given each one some money. Therefore, Mum came to the decision she would not give any money to any of them. She managed to get everywhere fast, whereas Dad and I took an hour to get from one shop to another, as we didn't have the heart to refuse them. Mum learnt fast to say, with one wave of her hand, '*Jao jao*' ('Go, go'). Apologies for being so mean about Mum's Hindi vocabulary. I stand corrected: she learnt *three* Hindi words the whole time she was there.

Everyone from home kept asking me to describe India to them. Soon my romantic view of the city and India faded. The vibrant colours were blocked out by the poverty and cruelty I saw every day. We were very lucky, as we lived a privileged life in India but we would have had to walk around blindfolded, not to notice the India we experienced. Sometimes I thought Mother did just that but then I realised that she became immune to the poverty so soon, that it did not affect her. I never became immune to it and couldn't understand how she did it.

When ensconced in our beautiful house and gardens, we saw nothing of the real India but we didn't have to take more than three steps out of the gate, before we would trip over a man carrying live chickens upside down on his cycle, a beggar asking for a few rupees or a young girl of barely twelve, selling balloons just so she could eat her next meal. It was heart-breaking and I constantly tried to shut out the poverty and degradation, desperation and sadness. It literally broke my heart, so I tried not to think about it, let alone write about it to describe it to people back home.

On one occasion soon after we got there, we were on our way back from an Embassy dinner at midnight. We stopped at some traffic lights and I happened to see a little boy of perhaps five or six years old, clearing up in a cafe after it had closed. He was working at midnight. He should have been in bed asleep and all he should have been thinking about, was what games he was going to play at school the next day. Yet he was working at midnight and had probably never set foot in a school. I could feel tears start to roll down my face, involuntarily. I tried not to let Mother and Father see this as Mum would most definitely have said something unsympathetic like, 'Well, what do you expect when there are so many of them?' And Father would make a stock statement each time we spoke about these things: 'What can you do, darling?'

That night I cried and cried into my pillow. I felt sad, helpless and desperately upset. That image stayed with me for a long time. I used to wish I could be like Mum and care a little less. For then, it wouldn't have upset me to see little children daily, walking around with no shoes and barely any clothes on. My stomach wouldn't turn each time I saw a mother sitting on the side of the road feeding her toddler with plain, boiled rice and I wouldn't have spent sleepless nights thinking about the cruelty that was meted out to animals in that country. When human life was so cheap and expendable, then the animals did not even feature on the radar of any type of humanity.

As I was fourteen, I guess that was deep enough thinking for me because life did carry on despite this.

The other cultural part of India that I loved when I first got there, but which soon started to irritate me, was I would often be woken up by either songs or speeches over the loudest loudspeakers possible. As a secular country, no one dared curb another person's freedom to annoy and deafen everyone else in their vicinity with their prayers, rantings, songs of celebration or anything else they deemed necessary, to shout out through their loudspeakers.

If I could avoid it, I didn't walk anywhere, as coupled with the fact that there seemed to be open drains everywhere, urinating on the road was the national pastime. Yet in the Indian constitution it was deemed a crime to *kiss* in public! Hence as I said, it was a country of extremes that did not make any sense at all. But that was what was so fascinating and kept me curious and wanting to know more and more, about what made this huge, chaotic country function and tick. I even loved the things that annoyed me about it. However I grew very much to love this land of diversity, joy and sadness. It added a richness to my life that helped shape me in more ways I can explain. It was then, and always will be my home from home where I go back to when I want to feel love, joy, safety and peace.

Mum did not care to have any in-depth conversations regarding the country or its people. Dad thought it was good education for me and therefore we discussed its politics and people at every opportunity. Even at a young age, I had very strong views about the differences between our different ways of life and was absolutely fascinated with the Indian way of life and their customs and beliefs, having come from a country and family that barely had any.

My father used to say that we could only do our best to help and kept harking back to the Golden Age of India's Independence and how one of his great heroes was Gandhi. He talked about how we now had to wait for the right people, like Gandhi, to be in charge again to make a difference in India.

I argued and assured him that the right people will never be in charge, as there are too many of the wrong people who will bring them down.

It reminded me of a joke Mr Raju had told me and it would have been funny if it wasn't so true.

An English fishery imported live crabs from all over the world, including from India. Each time they received a case from other parts of the world, the crates were nailed down so the crabs couldn't get out. Each time cases arrived from India, they were completely open with no lids, yet each time they checked and counted the crabs they were all accounted for. Finally, after months of this, the Englishman who received the crabs could not contain his curiosity any longer and called the Indian supplier. 'Tell me,' he said. 'How is it that the crates for crabs from the rest of the world have to be nailed down, to stop the crabs from crawling out, yet yours arrive open, with not a single crab missing.'

The Indian supplier said, 'Sir, these are Indian crabs. If one of them tries to climb out, the others pull him back down.'

For all my ranting and criticism of India and Hyderabad, I loved it so much that I vowed to go back and live there one day. It gradually seeped into every pore of my body, became part of me and I became part of it. I wanted to immerse myself in everything and embrace all I could of India.

'Who is Mr Raju,' you ask? I'm sorry, have I not introduced you to Mr Raju yet? How remiss of me! What can I tell you about him? He was one of my greatest influences in India.

Postcard No. 10
Love Thy Neighbour (Mum Couldn't!)

Next door to us — when I say, 'next door', the houses were half a mile away from each other — there lived a lovely South Indian family: the head of the family, the father Mr Raju, his wife and four children, the youngest of whom was a boy.

"In our families we must have a boy," said Mr Raju.

He loved to practise his English on us at every opportunity. If we asked him for a favour, 'I will comfortably do that for you,' was the answer. He was the most helpful person and constantly sent food over whenever he thought one of us was looking a bit peaky or flushed, or any colour at all. He laughed at the fact that, 'Western peoples turning red when in sun, they are going green when they are sick and white when they are scared. And they are calling us *coloured*! I am always black, is it not, Madam?' he would say to Mum, who would try to see the funny side.

Boundaries were not something Mr Raju knew much about, which Mother found very difficult to live with as she was never one for 'dropping in' to people's houses and she certainly did not expect anyone to 'drop in' to see her, without a fortnight's notice and preferably an application in triplicate. So, having Mr Raju next door was not conducive to the way she was used to living.

Mr Raju would drop in, unannounced, at any time of the day or night. For example, one day Mr Raju heard that Dad was going back to the UK via Dubai. He rushed over with some exceptionally important information to tell Dad.

"Mr Baxter, Sir, Mr Baxter, are you going to Dubai, Sir?"

"Affirmative," was Dad's reply.

"Okay, Mr Baxter, Sir, do *not* buy anything from Dubai, Sir. I am hearing that everything in Dubai is 'furious'." (Translation - 'Spurious')

Father assured him he would not be buying anything in Dubai as it was just a layover. It took over half an hour to explain what this meant to Mr Raju before he realised it was not something terribly obscene and he finally left us in peace.

I feel at this point I must pause and take you back to how it all started...

Postcard No. 1
Fibroids Uncovered

It was late 1960s England. Man had already walked on the moon, JFK had been shot and The Beatles had world domination. That's all the context you need really.

Both of my parents came from hugely academic families in Oxford, which I have never been allowed to forget. 'Don't you know your grandfather was an eminent barrister? Even the judges used to differ to him on points of law...' 'Don't you know your great-grandfather was a Don at Oxford and your great-great-grandfather...? And your grandmother...'

My parents met at college — and no, you're wrong!

You would automatically think Oxford, wouldn't you? But no, they met at Cambridge! Of course, if not Oxford, then it had to be Cambridge. And that's all the background you need.

Now let's talk about me.

Ever since I was a wee sprogette, I had been told — and all my friends had been told, relatives had been told, strangers had been stopped in the street at gun point and made to listen — that I was a miracle baby.

Mother was the fibroid type. She was *with child* but she was also *with fibroid*. Apparently, the fight for custody of the womb between the fibroid and the egg was very much like the fight between a mongoose and a snake — the mongoose (and the fibroid) always won.

Therefore, it was with a heavy heart that the doctor told

Mother that the little twinkle in her tummy would not survive. However, I was told that from there on, my mission in life started. The very reason I was born, the essence of my being… to prove everyone wrong.

As Mother waited tearfully for the inevitable to happen, it didn't. She just kept growing and growing. Finally, refusing to believe it was just weight she was putting on, Mother went to the doctor to find out whether she was going to be the first woman to give birth to an eight-pound fibroid instead of a baby.

After a short examination of Mother, shock and horror ensued. The doctor summoned every medical student he could find — and Mother swears there was even a cleaner in there somewhere, dragged in due to the confusion with the white coats — and each and every one of them had their hand up Mother within minutes. This was because, unluckily for Mother and the doctors, this was pre-ultrasound days, so the conventional method of gloves and KY Jelly was widely used.

Pretty soon, once the whole medical profession had got to know Mother intimately, inside out, it was officially announced that the fibroids had *miraculously* — I would like you to remember that word because I have never been allowed to forget it! — moved out of the way and that a child would be born after all.

And so, began the story of my birth.

I was so determined to come out that I must have negotiated my way around the fibroids and talked them into seeing sense. This has been said more times, than *The Sound of Music* has been aired over Christmas.

Postcard No. 2
A Typical Childhood

We were a typical family, though I have never understood what that means. There was my father, Anthony Charles Oliver and my mother, bizarrely named Vera Lynne — something she had to live with all her life — as her mother had been a huge fan of the singer.

Dad was slim, tall and good-looking. Mum had a beautiful face and used to be slim. After my birth, her figure took on a more rotund shape due to the fact that whenever she did battle with a chocolate bar, the chocolate won. Then there was miraculous me — Charlotte Emily.

As a result of the ever-present fibroids that moved aside just enough to enable my delivery into this world, I remain to this day, an only child, as my mother could not have any more children. Spoilt by my father and disciplined by my mother, they created the perfect balance. I learnt from an early age that I could wrap my father around the tip of my little finger as I was his little princess.

Most people, old and young alike, doted on me. I was an obedient child, though that didn't last very long and ended during Freud's fourth stage — Young Adult.

In the family, we also had two Boxers: Rufus and Beulah, who were a couple, as well as the obligatory, perverse bitch — no, not Mother! — a Dachshund called Suzie.

Mother called everyone 'Darling'. I was 'Darling', Dad was 'Darling' and the dogs were 'Darlings'. No one ever knew who she was referring to till we heard the tone of her voice. 'Darling!' shouted in a tone indicating 'I need help' or exasperation, was for Dad. 'Darling' said in a voice that meant 'Could you come here as I need to talk to you about something?' was usually for me.

The confusing part was her 'DAHAHLINGS!' said in an excited tone, which could either mean lunch had been served for the dogs or she had something to tell both Dad and me. So, there were times in the day, when all five of us would be at her side at once. This annoyed her greatly and she was quite adamant that all her 'darlings' sounded different.

By and large I had an exciting childhood.

There was the time when I was eight and along with a few friends, I decided to see what would happen if we chewed a packet of gum and then stuck it on our heads. As the experiment had been a complete failure as we couldn't get the gum out, we then decided to chop our hair off. Those of you who don't believe in a hell, try getting gum out of your hair! For days after that we walked around looking... well, like kids who had got gum stuck in their hair and then had to chop it all off.

When I was nine, the family — our *close* family was a traditional, 'large and far spreading, English' family consisting of about one hundred point five people — went on a summer picnic. Most of the aunts ate prawn cocktail sandwiches and there must have been a sting in the tail because soon it was their tails that were stinging. I have not seen so many aunts rush to the loo at the same time, since Cousin Hannah had baked her chocolate-laxative-chip cake a few months earlier.

Once we got back home, in view of the exodus to the WCs, all the younger cousins, me included, decided to superglue the toilet lids down. Another experiment we learnt nothing from.

I guess that like this story, it just provided pure entertainment. Nothing more, nothing less.

Year Ten - another picnic, another year. We were at Grandma's house, which had a fairly large garden attached to it. In this garden there was a well and in this well there was some dirty water. All the family had taken refuge inside the house as it was a hot day. Cousin Benjamin threw a huge stone the size of Surrey into the well and then shoved me behind some bushes. Before we knew it, grandparents, aunts, uncles, husbands and wives, were swarming around the well like drunks around a midnight curry.

Having counted the children and finding me missing, one of the uncles, having had quite a bit of Russian (vodka) courage, decided to jump in to save me. Shortly after swimming around for a few minutes and throwing up from the stench and vodka, a rubber ring, in the form of Aunty Jean's piles tube, was thrown in to save him. By now many tears were being shed, many ears had been boxed and much blame was going around.

Once Ben thought he had seen enough he brought me out from behind the bushes. Suffice to say, Ben needed the pile tube for months after that. But we all agreed it was worth it, especially since we weren't the ones in pain.

Postcard No. 3
A Stitch in Time

My eleventh year was a particularly bad one as that was the year I went under the knife. It was the summer holidays again and cousins galore had descended from all over the country. We decided to go to the local lake to see if Grandpa Charlie's teeth would sink, if we weighed them down with Grandma Gwen's wet knickers. If you'd seen the size of her knickers you would have been wise not to bet against it! It was all very exciting. The knickers were attached to the teeth by some string and lowered into the water. They ballooned out and for a few scary moments we thought they would provide a float for the dentures. But once saturated, they took the teeth down with them to the bottom of the lake, never to be seen again. Amid the excitement of the last sighting of the teeth, as they sank, I suddenly doubled up in pain with the firm belief that this was divine intervention and that I was being taught a lesson.

I was rushed home, not out of concern for me but because they couldn't stand my screams any longer.

Dr Smith, an old family friend, was called in. When I say that, he was a friend of the family, but the family was not a friend of his. He had just been around so long; he was now a sort of fixture. He had some questionable methods of dealing with medical problems:

• Food should be chewed thirty-two times if you had indigestion.

- Cod liver oil should be drunk once a month to clear out your system.
- Praying always helped.

When I heard they were bringing in Dr Smith, I was convinced I was being paid back.

After much poking and prodding, he announced that I was very badly constipated and an enema should be administered at once, to put me out of my misery. By now I had paid back for any sins I had committed in this life and was going to commit in the next. This time, no amount of screaming helped. An enema it was.

But unfortunately, during the next two days the pain got worse and Dr Smith asked me to chew my food thirty-two times. By now, my worried parents decided to bring in a real doctor, presumably deciding that I had been punished enough.

The real doctor took one look at my tummy and said, "Are you trying to kill the girl? Her appendix is about to burst!"

High drama ensued. *ER* could have taken a storyline from that day in my life. My dear father ran up the hospital steps with the speed of a thousand gazelles, with me in his arms. There was no time to think. I was thrown onto a bed with wheels and before I knew it, I had been cut up, the offending, life-threatening appendix removed and I was duly stitched up.

The doctors were amazed at the size of my appendix as it was just about to burst inside me and decided, in their wisdom, that they would keep it in a jar to show me when I came to. As an eleven-year-old who had just had emergency surgery, One would hop to see the anxious face of a mother or the smiling face a father as the effects of the anaesthesia wore off. I had an eye-full of my own appendix as I came to.

"Isn't it amazing?" the surgeon gushed. "I have never seen

one like it. Truly amazing. You are a very lucky, young lady. We caught it just in time."

Lucky was the last thing I felt at that moment.

An opportunist from a very young age, in the days to come I made full use of my situation. I moaned a lot, made weepy noises and generally any sound effects that would bring my parents running to my bedside. However, once again, the age-old belief of 'what goes around comes around' was proved true. It was now time to remove the stitches.

I knew this was going to be painful, I just didn't know how painful it was going to be. I knew the stitches' removal was imminent when the doctor and Mother made feeble attempts to distract me. 'Oh, look at that lovely tree outside' and 'Are you missing school then?', 'Where are you going for your holidays this year? Are Mum and Dad taking you somewhere nice?' For goodness sake, I was eleven, not three and even then, they would not have fooled me!

All this time, the stitches were being pulled but didn't seem to be coming out and I was screaming louder than an Osmonds' fan (yes, this does show my age), the only difference was that I was in pain. Well, I suppose they were in pain as well, if they had to listen to 'Puppy Love'.

Suddenly the surgeon stopped. "Ooops!" he said.

"Ooops? What do you mean by ooops?" Mother asked. Then both Mum and I watched in horror as he pulled the stitches out from the *correct* end.

All this while he had been trying to pull the stitches through from the wrong end!

It's a shame really that this happened when it did, because if that had happened today and we lived in America, we would have been millionaires.

Postcard No. 4
Blood Sweat and Tears

Year twelve was another significant year. One day at school, a few of us were eating our lunch outside as it was a hot summer's day. I got up from where I was sitting and one of the spotty, snotty boys said, "Eeeew, you sat in oil and it's all over your bottom!"

All the boys were spotty and snotty when I was that age and my gang of gorgeous girls and I — or at least we thought we were gorgeous, though I am sure we were a bunch of awkward, pre-pubescent, stuck-up girls — barely used to tolerate their presence. Much turning up of the noses and looking skywards took place, each time they opened their mouths to speak to us and this time was no exception.

However, one of the girls noticed that they were telling the truth and my electric-blue bellbottoms had a huge patch of something on them. As I ran to the loo to try and delete the cause of my embarrassment, one of the teachers grabbed hold of me and asked me where I was going in such a hurry.

When I pointed to the 'grease' on my bottom, she smiled and said, "No, my dear, that's not grease..." to which I let out a huge sigh of relief, "it's just blood," to which I let out a huge bellow. I couldn't feel any pain but thought that I should if I was bleeding, so I concentrated hard but still there was no pain. Before I could ask any questions, I was whisked off to the nurses' room and there I was distracted once again while the nurse phoned my mother. I wished people would learn some new distracting techniques. I tried to look to see if perhaps my appendix had grown and burst again. You may mock, but this really was the Age of Innocence. Soon Mother was there and after a few minutes of whispering in the next room she came in and I asked her whether the appendix theory was possible.

She said, "No, darling, that isn't possible and the nurse wanted me to be the one to tell you that you have started getting your period." I was shocked. I was as shocked as any shocked twelve-year-old could be. It took a long ten minutes for this to sink in. Then panic set in. I couldn't have my period, I was too young; none of my friends had it, they couldn't be told about it. Could I not have it next year or the year after?

I demanded that this should go no further than this room and all present swore to honour my wishes. Of course, now I would be wiser and get them to sign a confidentiality agreement and then sue them if they didn't adhere to it, because no sooner had we got home when Emma, my best friend's mum, called to ask how I was and what had happened, as most of the class was talking about it, so Mum told her!

"But she's your best friend!" Mother said when I protested. "Surely you want her to know?"

"But you promised you wouldn't tell a soul!" Clearly Mother did not think of her as 'a soul'.

However, the worst ordeal was yet to come. When Father got back that evening, Mother started to whisper at him over dinner, with her hand at the side of her mouth. It annoyed me dreadfully when they did this as I was always sitting right there. How could they not realise I could hear every word?

Mother mouthed, "Lottie's little friend arrived today."

And Father said, with his hand trying to hide his mouth,

"What little friend and why are we whispering about it?"

"No, you don't understand, darling. Her little friend that comes every month."

Father by now was getting quite frustrated. "What's her name and why does she come here every month? And why have I not met her before this?"

"For goodness sake!" I screamed. "I started bleeding today. I got my period."

"All right, Lottie," Father said. "No need to shout about it." Then he chuckled to himself at his own little joke.

"And there's no need to whisper about it either as I can hear every word," I said.

Emma thankfully kept it a secret till every other girl in the class got their period and then I 'came out' as it were, about a year later.

A year later, was year thirteen. A significant enough of a year for any teenager. I was so grown-up. For me, three important things happened: I found a boyfriend, I found myself and I found out that if God did exist, he wasn't listening to me.

Postcard No. 5
And They Called It Puppy Love

My parents were the members of a very posh club and each Sunday they had Beer Garden dances. I was, of course, forbidden from going as I was 'too young'. Then all of a sudden, when I turned thirteen, I was deemed 'old enough'. (Parents! Go figure!)

For my thirteenth birthday, not only was I allowed to have my first pair of two and a half-inch stiletto heels but I had my first 'dance party' at home. Then the next Sunday, I was taken to the Beer Garden dance at the club, where I was allowed to avail myself of the garden and the dances but not the beer.

No sooner had I sat down, when I noticed a boy a few tables away staring at me. He was also with his parents who kept poking him in the ribs and looking in my direction.

Parents really should be sent on a week-long course where they have modules entitled: '*Good distracting techniques for children ages eleven, twelve and thirteen*', '*How to be subtle and not embarrass your children to death*' and '*How to keep your children's secrets*'.

Finally, the boy relented and started to walk in the direction of our table. I quickly turned away and tried to take part in the conversation. I had barely tuned in to what the chatter was about, when it stopped abruptly and everyone looked over my head. I turned around and he was there. The first words he uttered to me were, "I heard you box. Do you want to mate?"

Mother's jaw hit the floor with a thud and then

Christopher, as I later learnt that was his name, completely flustered, rephrased his sentence. "What I mean is, I heard that you were a bitch and was wondering if you want to get together with my dog."

This time Father shot up from his seat, as another thud of jaw hitting floor was heard from Mother. Chris gulped, took a deep breath and slowly said, "What I mean is, I heard that you had a female Boxer dog and was wondering whether it would be possible for her to meet my male Boxer dog?" He then heaved a sigh of relief; Father sat back down and helped Mother gather up her lower jaw.

They say first impressions last and Father always looked at Chris with an air of suspicion.

Our Boxers never hit it off but we did. Chris was my knight in blue Levi jeans because in those days, Levis impressed much more than any shining armour would have done. I was going to marry him, I declared to my parents. He was the one for me and I would be with him for the rest of my life. This I declared over lunch about a month after our first fateful meeting. My parents smiled at each other; a dreadfully irritatingly knowing smile that says, 'Yes, yes, we've heard it all before and you will get over it'. Parents take note: *all* teenagers *hate* that. And can I remind you that I *was* a teenager.

'Teenager!' That word was music to my ears. I was now a teenager and old enough to know that if I said I was going to spend the rest of my life with someone, then that was what I was going to do. But no amount of 'I am, I am, I am' could wipe that grin off their faces.

They'll soon be smiling on the other side of their faces when I walk down the aisle with him, I thought.

Chris and I were together for one year exactly, which I suppose you could call a lifetime for a teenager.

Postcard No. 6
It's Me!

Soon after I met Chris, my social life became very hectic. We were now a couple and strutted our stuff at each and every party we were invited to; but one party sticks out in my memory.

An aunt of mine had given me a tee-shirt as a present the day before and I decided to wear it to the party we were going, to on Saturday night. As we entered the house, I saw the shadow of a woman next to me. She had the most amazing breasts I had ever seen. I kept staring at the shadow but each time I moved, she did too. Then the penny not only dropped, but I heard a *kerching*! noise as well. It was me! I had breasts!

I turned and faced the other way to get a look at the other breast and found that was as gorgeous as the other one! I couldn't stop staring at my silhouette and even on the dance floor, took up a position where the light fell on me in such a way that I could see my shadow on the wall. Now I was not only a teenager but I had breasts as well. Could life get any better?

Sadly, approximately a year after I met him, my knight's blue jeans began to fade and chinks started to show in his armour. Chris started to become possessive of me and jealous of anyone and everyone, who took up my time apart from him. It got to the point where I had to ask Mother to lie for me and tell him I was working on a school project, even if I was going out with one of my girlfriends! He was adorable and I loved him but he had to go.

Postcard No. 7
In Every Life, Some Rain Must Fall

Ever since I could kneel, I was made to kneel by my bed and say my prayers each night and each night, I did this like a good little girl… till year thirteen.

It seems to me that Harry Enfield's character 'Kevin' must have been based on some reality. I screamed a lot more and did the traditional thing that all teenagers did — I went through the obligatory stage of hating my parents. It would have been rude not to.

It seemed to me that with puberty came the realisation that my parents knew nothing and I knew everything. Therefore, it only seemed fair that I should stop doing everything they told me to do and should start doing things the way I wanted to. One of my ways of rebelling — brats all over the world, eat your hearts out — was to instantly cease the kneeling and praying and I decided to say my prayers in a more comfortable position — that is, lying in bed — till one of the darkest days of my teenage years.

Beulah, our Boxer, was run over by a car when we were taking her for a walk one day. We all screamed in horror and ran to her side but no sooner had the car run over her hind legs, than she got up and walked off without a care in the world. The next day, however, she couldn't move the back half of her body; it was paralysed. Mother and Father rushed her to the vet and I was made to stay at home as I was too hysterical. That is another side effect of being a teenager: anything is a reason for hysteria. But this time I had good reason.

For the first time in many months, I threw myself down on my knees and prayed harder than I had ever done before.

An hour later my parents were back with Beulah in tow. She had been given a number of injections and we just had to wait and see. That night I knelt and prayed again. And during the next days, my knees became raw and chaffed. Each day, Beulah was taken to the vet to monitor her progress. On the fourth day, my parents returned without Beulah and I stopped praying for the rest of my life.

She had been put to sleep as her condition had worsened and it would have been cruel to keep her alive.

What about my prayers? I wanted to know. Where was God? Was he/she not taking calls at the time? Was he/she out? On holiday?

So now you know — that is how I came to be in my fourteenth year, happily settled in our new home, environment and country.

Postcard No. 11
It's Chui!

However, I do believe that maybe Beula did come back to us, sometime later in a different form. Shortly after we arrived in Hyderabad, Mother decided to have some work done on the house to make it more 'user-friendly' — her way of saying she wanted to make it more 'English'. One of the workers arrived with a small Chihuahua in tow, called Chui. She was adorable. We all doted on her and loved playing with her. She was thoroughly spoilt by us. Then one day he turned up without Chui. When we asked where she was, Mr Raju translated. Apparently, she had started foaming at the mouth and had suspected rabies, so the workman had left her in a field. We were devastated. As there were many stray dogs in India, we were fairly confident she wouldn't starve but that night, we were all very quiet at dinner and realised how attached we had got to the tiny little thing, even Dad.

A few weeks later, Mother and I were shopping at the local vegetable market when we saw this little dog running up to greet us! Chui! We have no idea where she came from and how she recognised us from a distance but she wasn't foaming at the mouth and nor was she sick. Mr Raju concluded she could have attacked a frog that might have made her foam at the mouth, as that's what frogs do when they are trying to defend themselves or it could have been a number of things. We had her checked by the local vet and having been given a clean bill of health, we brought her home to become part of the family.

Postcard No. 12
Mr Raju Again

It was 9 p.m. when Mr Raju turned up at the door one night. His brother-in-law's aunt's husband, on his father's side, had been in a coma for a week after a massive heart attack. He had now died and Mr Raju had come to give us the sad news. However, 'The doctor said, madam, that thanks be to God he died now or he would have been a vegetarian all his life!' We didn't like to correct Mr Raju and explain to him that he meant 'vegetable', as he felt his English was 'jolly good' and we didn't want to shatter that illusion.

"Could that not have waited till the morning?" said Mother, as we closed the door on him at 10.30 p.m., after we had heard the intricate details of how he had been operated on, how they had tried to save his life, how after he died the hospital had had the *audacity* (though that wasn't his word), to slip a birthing kit onto the bill as one of the tools used during the operation. "I said to the hospital, "Well, where is the baby then, sir, if you are using a birthing kit?" and then, Madam, they took it off the bill. I tell you, these Indians will try anything," he chuckled to himself, as he walked out the door.

Father and I thought that was hilarious but Mother was not amused. Oh, don't feel too sorry for Mum. She and Father, when the time was right, gave Mr Raju all the gory details of the fibroid saga. He listened with interest and in awe.

"And so, you see, that's why we call her our miracle baby. She just pushed the fibroids out of the way."

"Yes indeed," Mr Raju agreed. "You are right, Madam,

Sir, she is truly a miracle. For that reason, I am going to get a very famous *jotish* here in Hyderabad to do her horoscope. This must be done. As you say, she is a miracle and we must find out her path in life."

The *jotish* arrived a week later and it was Mother this time who said that we must be polite and accept this kind offer from Mr Raju, as he believed in horoscopes and it would be rude not to comply.

Mother had to give the *jotish* intricate and intimate details about my birth and he had to sit through the fibroid story as well. However, after that, there wasn't really anything more intimate she could disclose. After an hour of calculations and looking at my palms, the final calculations were complete and he began his predictions.

I was going to be widely travelled (what a revelation considering Father worked for the British Government), I was going to be very wealthy (yes, I liked that). I would suffer a grave tragedy in my life but having suffered this tragedy, my life would be smooth from then on. Well, I had already broken a well-manicured fingernail that week, so felt that was probably what he was referring to. And then I waited for it and yes, there it was, right at the end, — the sentence I had been waiting for that started with, 'You will be blessed with...'

The *jotish* puffed his chest out; he had clearly saved the best for last. "And you will be blessed with three sons."

Apparently, I was going to have twins to begin with and then another boy.

"Just kill me now," I said when he was done, which thankfully, was not understood by either Mr Raju or the *jotish* and after a dirty look from Mother, I thanked them both profusely and they went on their way.

Mr Raju felt very proud of himself, as he had now delivered unto me what my future would hold.

Postcard No. 13
Speaking of Vegetables

I was now fifteen and on one of our visits to the markets, I passed another life-changing milestone in my life. I loved going to the markets with Mother and Cook, as there was always so much to see. The bright colours of the vegetables were so vivid and looked positively glazed, as the vendors flicked water onto them. The noise, smells of spices and the bustling crowds tantalised all my senses at once. The meat and vegetable markets were kept separate, as some were very strict vegetarians in India and could not even cook vegetables in the same pans that meat had been cooked in.

We had just finished our shopping. Mother had forgotten to find out from her favourite vegetable vendor, when he was going to be getting the sugar snap peas, she had ordered from Ooty, a hill station in India; one of the cooler parts of the country.

Dan and Cook were loading the car and I looked across at the meat market. About ten feet away from me was a cage, locked from the outside and in this cage, there were chickens.

You see this sight all over India but these chickens were flapping all over the place and I couldn't understand why they were doing this, as they knew they couldn't get out. When I looked closer, I saw that they were all headless and blood was sprouting out from their necks. I jumped into the car and started screaming and screaming. Dan opened the driver's side and asked me what was wrong. I pointed to the chickens, still screaming.

Dan nodded knowingly. "Yes, child, it's not a nice sight, is it?" By now, I was hitting my head against the dashboard. I don't even remember doing this.

Dan decided he needed to go and fetch *Amma*, which is what he called Mother. '*Amma*' in Hindi could either mean 'mother' or 'madam'.

"I really am not old enough to be his mother," she would say indignantly but I think she secretly, liked the fact he called her that.

Mum was hurriedly brought over, then they all jumped in the car and took me home. The local doctor was called as I wouldn't calm down. "Well Madam, what we have here is a case of true hysteria," said the doctor.

"We have had that *many* times before but I have never seen her like this," said Mother

"No, madam," the doctor explained. "You see, most people nowadays use the word 'hysteria' very lightly and that is not its true meaning. When someone is truly hysterical, they actually lose control and this is what has happened here. She has had a terrible shock and I am going to give her something to calm her down." I slept for a good, few hours. When I woke up it was dinner time and guess what was on the menu? — roast chicken.

When Father got back home, Mother relayed the whole harrowing episode to him and then the whispering and hand-over-mouth saga started all over again.

Dad: "Darling, do you really think it was prudent to make roast chicken for dinner when she has just had this traumatic experience with chickens?"

Mum: "Don't be silly, darling. Roast chicken had already

been prepared and how was I supposed to know that she was going to have this experience? Do you really think that I would say, 'Oh Cook, why don't we prepare roast chicken for dinner in light of what just happened this afternoon? Perhaps it will take Lottie's mind of chickens for a while'?"

Dad: "Now, darling, there's no need to be sarcastic about it."

Mum: "Well, I'm sorry, darling. I've had an awful day. It was very upsetting."

Dad: "I know, darling but was it really such a horrible sight?" Mum: "Yes, it was and it affected Lottie terribly."

"Mum, Dad, I'm right here," I said. "You don't need to keep putting your hands over your mouths and you don't need to whisper. I can hear every word. When will you stop doing this?"

They carried on as if I wasn't there and they hadn't even heard me.

Dad: "Well darling, I think we had better remove it from the table, in case she sees it."

Mum: "But what do you propose I feed us? Why don't we ask her if she'll eat it?"

"*Mother*!" This finally got her attention.

"Sorry, darling, you were saying? I was talking to your father and didn't hear what you said."

"I know you were talking to Dad. I'm sitting right here at the table. I can hear you. I can't eat the chicken and I can't even look at it. I feel sick. I can't eat anything. Can I please be excused?"

"Yes, of course you can, darling. Why don't you go and lie down and I'll bring you a nice hot chocolate in a while?"

"No, thank you. I really don't want anything."

As I left the room, they started whispering again.

Dad: "Does that mean we can now eat the chicken, or do you think she wouldn't want us to eat it either?"

Mum: "Don't be ridiculous, darling. Of course we can eat the chicken but I think we should wait till she's gone into her bedroom. We don't want her to hear us tucking into it."

Dad: "Well, I don't see what difference that makes. The chicken is already dead and it isn't one of the ones from the cage."

I shook my head, closed my door and heard knives and forks clanging as I did so.

I would never eat meat again. That image would stay with me forever.

Postcard No. 14
It's A Dog's Life

I continued my education at a local school, as most schools followed the British syllabus and I made new friends easily, due to the fact that they were as intrigued by me and my life, as I was by theirs.

Mother continued to surround herself with people who were 'like -minded' and Father was constantly busy with work.

Chui proved to be worth her weight in gold for Mum, as she would send her into my room to wake me up each morning and being so small, Chui would be able to get under the covers, lick my face and nuzzle me till I was well and truly awake.

It was at Father's work where our other dog, Rover, was adopted. Dad noticed a dog tied up close to his office building for a few days in a row. He asked around but no one knew who this dog belonged to. The street vendor across the road said he had been feeding him and giving him water but wasn't sure who had tied him up and whether they were coming back to get him.

Father was fed up of this cruelty and let the dog go and told the street vendor, to let him know if the owner came back and he would have him thrown in jail. Of course, my dad didn't have such powers but the street vendor did not know that.

The next day, as Dad left the office at 5 p.m., the dog was waiting outside and started to follow him to his car. Father patted him and played with him. The next day was the same. And the next.

Each time father left the office,, the dog would be there at 5 p.m. One day, dad popped out at lunchtime to see if he was just hanging around and he wasn't. But in the evening, right on 5 p.m., there he was, waiting for Dad.

That day, Father came home with Rover. He was a very independent dog and although he liked the occasional pat and play, he wasn't really fussed about us. Chui, on the other hand, needed heaps of attention and fuss. When she met Rover, instead of being jealous and worried, she embraced him with all four paws and welcomed him into our home. Rover barely gave her a sideways glance. She wanted to play; he wanted to sleep.

One day, after Rover had been with us for a few weeks, when Dad was due to leave for work, Rover jumped into the car with him and sat on the seat, looking straight ahead. Father said to Daniel, "I think he wants to come to work with me."

So off they went. Rover got out at father's work and wandered off. Father was a bit perplexed and worried, so he asked Daniel to follow him. Rover rummaged around in bins and Daniel left him reacquainting himself with the street vendor. Father always came home for lunch and at lunchtime, Rover arrived at the car and gave Daniel a quizzical look as if to say, 'Well, go on. Open the door. I'm coming home for lunch!' Shortly afterwards Father turned up at the car, amazed to see Rover sitting in the car looking straight ahead.

Rover came home for lunch and then went back with Father to work. This continued for many days.

Daniel used to joke, "You know, sir, I was hired to drive you but if I told my mother I was driving a dog, she would be very upset!"

One day Rover did not budge in the morning. What was

wrong with him? Was he sick? Father tried to put him in the car but he jumped out again. Mother and I took him to the vet and explained to him the strange phenomenon that was Rover. He laughed and said, "There's nothing wrong with him, Madam. Has your husband noticed him sleeping under cars in the afternoon?"

"Why, yes," said Mother. "Just the other day my husband said that when he came home for lunch, Rover was already at the car, but asleep under it."

"Well Madam, you have a very clever, stray dog here. He now does not want to go with your husband to work as it is too hot for him to roam around. He now just wants to stay at home where it's cool!"

And so, we continued to marvel at our amazing Rover.

Postcard No. 15
And Dowry Is Illegal, Madam

The one constant, ever-present presence was Mr Raju, who kept coming over to delight us with his amazing 'chatter'. We had been invited many times to his house for dinner and he to ours, but he could never get enough of us. This time, he came over to tell us the 'very good news' about his eldest daughter's wedding.

Although dowry is illegal in India, it still happened behind closed doors. I was always fascinated by Mr Raju's revelations. He came to tell us all about the arrangements. He huddled us together and said that he was about to tell us a huge secret. "I will tell to you something," he said, "but you, please, do not give tongue to it." (Translation – Confidential)

What was the *big* secret that we must not *give tongue* to? Well, the big secret was that because his daughter was so tall and dark, they had found it difficult to find a groom for her. "We were very lucky to get an engineer for five lakhs." (Five thousand pounds, which in the late 1970s was a princely sum in India.)

I wanted to tell him that he needed to get out more and move in our circles, especially with Mum's chums!! *Their* gossip was enough to make a sailor blush. And they certainly *did* give tongue to everything they heard. In fact, they gave so much tongue, I was surprised it hadn't worn out yet!

He told us about the ceremony and how when the bride tried to garland the groom, he would try to move away and didn't let her put the garland on first time. The reason for this was that the boy should not relent the first time, because to be garlanded he would have to bow his head and if he bowed his head to her, then he would be doing that his whole life. Obviously, equality for women had not reached those parts yet. I wanted to tell him that Mother wouldn't have even tried to get Father to bow his head with a garland, she would have just used a crowbar!

And so, our fascination with Mr Raju and India continued.

Postcard No. 16
Let's Call It 'Operation Operation'

We spent the next five years in India, immersing ourselves in every aspect of life there. Well, when I say *we*, I mean Dad and me. Mum didn't, as much as she tried to come to grips with the language, the food or the climate. Father always joked that Mother would have been the worst person to kidnap. They would have given her back without gaining a ransom as she was such high maintenance. He loved that joke and told it at many of his Government functions.

The rest of my schooling was fairly uneventful and not being a natural student, I got through each year by the skin of my teeth. I had a lot of fun though.

At one point my parents were convinced I would be a doctor, owing to my unnatural penchant for all things gory and medical.

However, I didn't have a choice, as over the next few years my parents were in hospital, having one operation or another. So, I *had* to take an interest. In the end they named a wing after us, not because we donated it but because we were there so much. We knew all the doctors by their first names and they were part of our Christmas card list.

One particular operation in my sixteenth year, is lodged in my memory. Mother developed two cysts: one in her eye and one in her lower (very lower) abdomen. She insisted it was due to the food and the pollution.

The doctor, who had spent ten years studying to be a

doctor and specialised in cysts and all things alien in the body, was clearly wrong, as he gave Mother another explanation: that some people are just predisposed to cysts and some are not. There could be many factors which had contributed to this but he would not include pollution and a certain type of food in those factors.

However, Mum was not convinced. The cysts had to come out and the doctor in his wisdom decided to remove them both at the same time.

Mum was put in a large hospital gown.

As they were going to operate on her eye and her nether regions at the same time, I tried to convince Mother to write 'Mind the Gap' on her thighs but she refused. Then I begged her to write 'Keep off the Grass' but in the end gave up for fear of my own life and lumps.

As mentioned earlier, being on first name terms with the doctor I thought he would let me in to the operating theatre this time. No such luck but I am sure he must have been in some way, related to the doctor who operated on my appendix because no sooner had the operation finished, when he sent out a glass jar for me with his commiserations and apologies for not letting me view the operation but was sending the next best thing with his compliments — Mother's cysts in a jar!

They were fascinating and I made a pretty penny over the next few weeks charging one rupee per viewing. There was an added bonus as well. Guests who came for dinner post the op, kept playing around with their food and examining it as I had spread the rumour that Cook loved to experiment with various food groups and kept the jar in the kitchen for inspiration.

The only drawback to this whole incident, was the aftercare at the hospital. The nurses did not speak English very well and with Mother's fantastic command of Hindi we ended up with a *Mr Chary's* prescription for heart problems. It was only when we got the tablets home, that we realised they had given us the wrong ones. But what of the poor people who can't read in India? I do hope Mr Chary could, or he would have been taking Mum's tablets to avoid cysts in the future. If he could read, he must have been completely flummoxed as to when he had developed those cysts and why he hadn't been told about them and might have been desperately trying to examine his abdomen, trying to find it. Sorry, Mr Chary!

The next year I was seventeen and Mother celebrated by breaking her leg. She never did things in halves and so didn't just break it but smashed her kneecap to smithereens.

Out of boredom, Mum decided to start a Dramatics Society where bored housewives like herself, could become involved with a little drama (!) and put on shows for the local community. Mother said she was 'bringing a bit of culture to India'.

I tried to tell her that they had practically invented culture and had been carving the most intricate and awe-inspiring temples and statues in the seventh century, while we in the UK thought the height of culture was to thump a woman on her head and drag her into a cave. Come to think of it, we hadn't changed much really.

She had only just started the Society and was about to put on her first show — a series of skits she had written.

She was congratulating the cast on a great achievement and telling them how proud she was of them and just before the play started, she said, "Break a leg." They all looked at her horrified. She then explained to them that it was a saying in the theatre world, where you said 'Break a leg' before a play and it was good luck. They then all proceeded to turn to each other and say 'Break a leg'. Mother stepped backwards to get off the stage, tripped over a wire, tumbled down the stairs and broke her leg and smashed her knee to smithereens.

The cast felt she had really gone the extra mile to give them luck.

Her knee had to be operated on. Once it was all over and everyone was over the shock, the surgeon came to examine Mother and to see how it was all healing. "Doctor, when will I be able to walk?" she asked him, anxiously.

His answer: "Oh, you want to walk?"

After she heard this, it took us about a day and half and all the chocolate in Belgium, to calm her down!

Back at home, Cook and Maid insisted on using their own medicine on Mother to try and heal her knee at a quicker pace.

You could always tell when someone was not well in Hyderabad, as they were usually multicoloured.

There was *lal dava* (red medicine) for cuts and *kala dava* (black medicine) if you had a boil in your mouth. Turmeric, which left a yellow stain, was widely used as an antiseptic and for numerous other things. So, whenever you saw someone that looked like a rainbow you knew for sure they were not very well.

In my eighteenth year, it was Father's turn and *his* knee. He injured his knee in such a way that they had to replace it. He loved golf and any spare time he had you would find him on the golf course. This particular day started off with someone else getting injured. Father was playing with a novice and trying to show him that there was nothing more enjoyable in the world than golf, not even sex. Golf was the new sex.

As the novice hit his first stroke, the ball flew into the air and a few seconds later they heard a loud screech. They ran towards the sound and saw a large man rubbing the head of a very slim lady. Dad and the novice started to apologise profusely and as they did so, the man stopped rubbing the lady's head, turned to Father and said in a broad Texan accent, "Hey, are you British?" Father confirmed this.

By this time, the large, Texan man had forgotten all about his wife's head and started talking to Dad. "Hey, Man, I lurve your accent, man."

The lady rightly interjected by pointing out to her husband that there was still the issue of the ball attacking her. Her husband turned to her and said, "Don't worry, honey. When you say you have a headache tonight, this time I'll believe ya!"

He was so thrilled at the joke he had just cracked that the large Texan smacked Father on the back, as if to say, 'Don't you think that was funny?' and literally swept him off his feet. Dad went tumbling down a hill and cracked his knee open on a stone.

Once again, the surgeon, now a family friend, conducted the operation but not before a couple of predictable jokes about 'Oh, it's the right leg? No, the left leg? Is it the knee? Or the ankle?'

The operation took three hours. Finally, the surgeon came out to see us and said it had been a huge success, that Dad's bones were very strong, he was young and healthy and also his joints were flexible, so there should be no problems. He had also taken some pictures of the knee while operating and showed them to us. Dad was not smiling in any of them, which was very disappointing.

His stay in hospital was stressful to say the least. However, the good news was that if I needed drugs to stay sane, hospitals were the best place to get them. The bad news? They only gave them to the patients and the drugs Dad was on were not strong enough for me.

If visiting a hospital in Hyderabad, here are a few things that you need to remember:

1. Make sure you speak all the South Indian languages as each nurse and employee there speaks a different one. They can't communicate with each other and they communicate with you with difficulty.

2. Make sure you take some strong drugs to steel your nerves, because every half an hour you will have a visit from either a doctor, nurse technician, cleaner or supervisor to ask you how things are and when you tell them, they go away and do absolutely nothing about it.

3. Don't have an emergency on a Sunday as they don't have the staff to cover it.

The pièce de résistance was the conversation Father had with one of the training nurses. Usually, when the nurses came over to take his blood pressure, they took his temperature as well. One day, one of the training nurses came to do this and this is how the conversation panned out once she had taken Dad's blood pressure.

Dad: "Are you not going to take my temperature?"

Training Nurse: "No."

Dad: "Oh, normally the nurses take my temperature after they've taken my blood pressure."

Training Nurse: "Do you have a thermometer?"

Father: "No, of course not."

Training Nurse: "Then how can I take it?"

However, all in all the stay was not too bad: they didn't kill him and for that I was grateful.

Once we were back home, I reflected on my time looking after Father and the one thing I learnt about myself, is that I could *never* be a full-time nurse, no matter how much I was paid. I'm just not that caring.

Father's leg wasn't stitched but stapled. Apparently, this was the latest in post-operative etiquette. Stitches were so last season. Mother asked if she could get some for my mouth, but they said they don't believe in cruelty to animals.

Postcard No. 17
Mayhem On The Minar Express

As I was now eighteen, I decided it was time to brave the Indian Railways I had heard so much about and I decided to visit Bombay, as my first foray into the country on my own. No book about India (no matter what the topic) would be complete, without at least a story or anecdote about the Indian Railways. So here it is.

When I first went to India I was horrified by the poverty, delighted by the weather, saddened by the cruelty to animals and people, angered by the corruption, pleased with the friendliness of the people, curious about the languages and amazed by the rituals and religions. I lived through all these emotions and feelings but travelling on a train from Hyderabad to Bombay, enabled me to experience these emotions all in one go during my twelve-hour journey. (Minar '*Express*'??)

I was told I hadn't lived, unless and until, I travelled by train in India and I certainly wanted to go back to old Blighty and say I had lived. Therefore, I found myself being driven to the station to catch my train.

As we approached the station, Dan turned to me and as usual said, "Traffic jam ho gaya Madam." This always means so much more than he says. What he actually says is - 'There is a traffic jam Madam', but what he means is — 'Well now's a good time to get out 'War and Peace' and read it twice', or it could mean, 'I think it would be quicker for you to walk to where you want to go'. In this instance I got out. Daniel left the car in the middle of the road in order to help with my luggage and we started to edge our way towards the station. Coolies stormed us from every direction in their faded red uniforms, red turbans and shiny brass armbands. They screamed and shouted at us, asking if there was any luggage to be carried. When the answer was yes, they then screamed and shouted amongst themselves as to who would carry it. By the time we arrived at the station, I presumed it was mutually agreed and we had a coolie.

Dan tipped his hat to say goodbye but what he really meant was 'good luck' and 'sooner you than me' and he was off.

Pushing through the crowd and bundles on the floor, I reached the information chart board where I checked the platform number.

Before long, I was seated on the train. It was a standard, one-class train and offered the pleasure of travelling with all kinds of people. There were three-tier berths on either side of each compartment and my berth number was on my ticket, indicating where I would sleep at night.

However, the lower berths were where everyone sat during the day and as luck would have it, I had one of the lower berths. I paid the coolie, settled in and started to size up my co-passengers.

There was a family of five: husband, wife and three sons. The wife was pregnant again hence, soon to be a family of six. There was also a lady and her four-year-old daughter. We smiled at each other and the train began to move. It was 4 p.m.

Everything was peaceful and I was enjoying my book until 7 p.m.

That's when the family of five-going-on-six took out their

'tiffin': a lunchbox of layered pans to carry hot food. This was not a family who believed in fast food.

First came the rice, then the dal, then two curries, samosas and poppadoms and finally, sticky, *goolab jamoons* — a delicious but fattening (with a lot of stress on the 'fattening' part) Indian sweet.

Having laid all this out on the berth I was to sleep on, they began to tuck in.

First the lentils slipped onto the berth, then some rice. By this time, I had taken out my measly little sandwich and was nibbling on it. The gentleman being very kind and hospitable like all Indians are, gave me some *goolab jamoons* on a plate saying, '*Khao, khao*' (eat). He probably felt sorry for me seeing I only had a sandwich to eat. Not wishing to be rude, I thanked him and ate it, wondering how many sit-ups I was going to have to do to burn it off. Finally, at the end of the meal, the sticky sauce from the *goolab jamoon* also found its way onto the berth. So, when the wife asked me if I would mind sleeping on the top berth instead of her as she had difficultly climbing up, I readily agreed.

At 9 p.m., I climbed onto my berth, fell asleep and slept quite soundly until I head a yell loud enough to be heard over the engine noise and the train's thundering and rattling on the tracks. It was the youngest son of the family of five. He needed the toilet. His father was trying to get him to go back to sleep, telling him it was all in his mind but when he refused to accept this, his father woke his mother who was in a deep sleep and asked her to take him to the toilet! I looked at my watch. It was half past midnight.

All was quiet again until, "Psssss. Pssssss. Pssssss." I looked down from my berth to see the mother with the four-year-old. She had seated her daughter on a portable potty and was chanting, "Pssss. Psssss." When she saw me looking down, she said in a whisper, "She cannot sit on the bathroom pot so am trying to make her go here."

"Really? I would have never guessed," I muttered to myself.

"Pssss, Pssss," she carried on.

Finally, I couldn't stand it any longer — I had to go!

When I got back from the loo, the lady gave me a big grin and said, "She went."

I gave her an even bigger grin and said, "So did I."

It was 2 a.m.

I fell asleep again until the train stopped at a station and I was woken up to the clanging of steel and the clinking of glasses, accompanied by, "Chai, chai, coffeeya, coffeeya!"

I got off the train in Bombay, dirty and dusty from the soot I had collected along the way, sleep-deprived and weary. I said goodbye to my travelling companions, headed straight for the refund counter and bought a plane ticket home.

Yes, it was an experience I wouldn't have missed for the world but no, I didn't want to do it again.

Postcard No. 18
It Must Be Love, Love, Love

As I had finished school, I decided to do a Psychology degree and spent the next few years learning about the human mind and how it ticked.

I was in my nineteenth year, when part of my life changed forever. I was at a party with my parents. It was terribly boring, with lots of armed forces personnel and Government bigwigs, all of whom were trying to prove their wig was bigger than the next person's. The protocol was driving me mad as no one could sit down before the general and then the general's wife had to begin the meal. Then, you couldn't leave the table before the general but what if you needed to pee? Which, as luck would have it, I now needed to.

As I got up to go to the toilet, I was stopped by a flunky to say I had to wait till the general had finished. I tried to explain to him in Hindi that I needed the toilet but he didn't understand. I was about to explain to said flunky that there would be a very wet patch on the floor that very second if he did not let me go, when all of a sudden, a hand grabbed my arm and I heard something being muttered in Telugu (the local language I hadn't quite mastered) to the flunky and I was whisked away and planted safely outside the toilet door. I looked up at my saviour.

He was the most beautiful creature I had seen in my entire life. I could never have imagined that something so beautiful could exist. I barely found the words to thank him and ran into the loo, not knowing whether it was my bladder or my flushed face that needed attention.

Afterwards, when I looked at myself in the mirror I thought, Mr Raju is right, we are *coloured*! I had turned into the ripest, red tomato.

When I finally thought I had turned a more normal shade of red, I gingerly opened the toilet door half-expecting him to be there but he wasn't. I desperately tried to find him that evening, without being too obvious but failed. Just before we were leaving — and owing to protocol, we couldn't depart until the general and his wife had left — I finally saw him.

I asked the lady next to me, "Why is that young man allowed to walk out as well? I thought everyone had to wait for the general."

"Yes," said the lady, "but he's their son."

That night I tossed and turned and turned and tossed and all I could think about, was him. I dreamt of him and couldn't get his face out of my conscious or unconscious mind. I felt sick. I felt excited. I felt upset, worried, sweaty, completely wretched and joyous all at the same time. I sat bolt upright in bed. Was this what they called being head over heels in love?

I had experienced a mild version of this with Chris: a few butterflies, a few squeaks, a few blushes, my heart doing a few little jumps. But this was different. The butterflies were now doing loop the loop in my tummy, the squeaks had turned to squawks, the blushes were burning my face and my heart was doing somersaults on a trampoline.

The next morning, I tried to find out from Dad how well he knew the general.

"Not very well," he said. "We know each other in passing as we meet at work sometimes and at these sorts of dinners.

Why the sudden interest, Lottie?"

I hated that nickname but Father loved it and got into quite a muddle at times, trying not to use it and would start by saying 'Lot... Char... lottie', which made it worse. This time, I didn't even bat an eyelid as he went on to tell me the wars in which the general had fought and the medals he had won.

"'I thought you were bored yesterday and hated it. You told me so enough times last night, so why do you ask?"

'Because I am only interested in his son. He is the most amazing thing I have ever seen. I think I fell in love with him last night and I want to meet him again *now*!' is what I wanted to say but instead I said, "Oh, no reason really."

For the next three weeks, I sat through many a boring dinner insisting I accompany Dad, even when Mum could not be bothered due to the Richter-scale boredom being so high. But none were fruitful.

Finally, I gave up and asked Dad where the general was and why he had not graced a single of these dinners. I was even prepared to tell him the reason I wanted to know. Father said he had gone to Switzerland with his family for a holiday and gave me a quizzical look but I left the room before he had time to ask me why.

A week later, I got a call from my friend Annu who was having an eighteenth birthday party, which we had all been looking forward to this for ages. It was a *big bash* at her house, with a live band, fireworks and a mime. She called me to ask a favour. A boy who had apparently seen me at another party had been asking her to introduce me to him. She had been putting him off but could put him off no longer and would I please meet him, so that he would stop bothering her. I grudgingly told her to tell him he could pick me up for her party. She thanked me profusely and told me that the boy would be thrilled.

I was ready the next day at 7.30 p.m. and as I waited, I heard a roar outside the front door. I opened it and saw a huge motorbike pull up. The rider had his helmet on and I looked at the scene in disbelief. If this was my escort, he had more of a chance of getting Mother on the back of that than me in my party dress. He parked up, removed his helmet and smiled. I never knew what swooning meant till that day. I nearly passed out and for the first time, it wasn't because I had tried to get in a dress two sizes too small for me. It was *him*... my toilet hero!

That evening, neither of us had any sense of anyone else even being at the party. Annu was most disappointed at my lack of enthusiasm for the fireworks but how could I be, when there were far more tremendous explosions going off in my head?

His name was Zaheer Modi. His family were Parsees. I wanted to know everything there was to know about him. His religion was Zoroastrianism and the family originated from Persia. Zoroastrianism was the oldest monotheistic religion in the world. Their prophet, Zarathustra, was said to be the first ever environmentalist; I guess the predecessor to the Green Party, four thousand years ago. They believe that fire purified and therefore Zoroastrians revered fire. Zoroastrianism teaches you to "Never desecrate the fire, don't destroy the earth and do not pollute the sweet waters of the world."

The Parsees were an ethnic minority group in India. In the 1600s they had been persecuted by the Arabs and fled across the desert, some to Europe but the majority had come to India. This group of Persians were mainly from a place called Parse in Persia and hence were called 'Parsese', which means 'from

75

Parse'.

Some of them, of course, died crossing the desert and to avoid the Arabs catching up with them and desecrating the bodies, they placed them up at the highest point they could so that the vultures would devour them before the Arabs could reach them; believing they had come from nature and would go back to nature. This tradition has carried forward till today, as the Parsees traditionally bury their dead by leaving them in places called 'Towers of Silence' for the vultures to eat off the remains, "No way am I going to be plucked at by a mangy scavenger," Zaheer used to say.

Once across the desert they arrived at a small place called Sanjaan in Gujarat and asked for refuge. The king at that time said they were crowded enough as it is and in order to illustrate this, he sent the leader of the Parsees an earthen container full to the brim with milk, which I guess meant they were full to capacity. The leader of the Parsees took a spoonful of sugar and mixed it into the milk without spilling a drop. He said that the Parsees would be like the sugar in the milk: 'We will blend in with your people without upsetting the equilibrium but we will also sweeten them'. The king was so impressed he let the Parsees in but with certain conditions:

- They had to adapt to Indian dress and learn Gujarati.
- They could not marry before sundown (most Indian weddings took place before then).
- They were forbidden from converting anyone to their religion.

"The most famous Zoroastrian by far is Freddy Mercury, who was born Farookh Balsara," Zaheer told me.

We did not stop talking and laughing till 4 a.m., when he finally dropped me at my door. He leant over to kiss me. We were surrounded by moonlight and mosquitoes, which were biting me all over but I was not going to let them spoil this special moment. He kissed me and I heard a loud roar go off in my head and then realised I had moved the throttle of his bike too far, by leaning back on it.

I was in love and had never known anything like it. They say to love each other isn't enough; you have to love things together. And we did. We liked the same music, the same food, the same movies... The list was endless. For a nineteen-year-old, he was wise beyond his years. He talked about philosophy and literature and music like it had always been such a part of his life.

What I loved most about him was his passion for everything: buildings, bikes, the poor, the deprived, the privileged, flowers, temples, songs. He described and felt everything with such passion, I could not help but be carried away with everything he said and did. He talked about all he wanted to achieve and the things he would like to do. He wanted to travel the world, to see all the places he had read about in books and experience everything, from swimming with dolphins to hang-gliding off the Corcovado Mountain in Rio.

The icing on the cake were his wonderful parents, who were loving, caring, affectionate, funny and generous. They welcomed me with open arms and made me feel as warm as feet against a radiator on a cold day.

Postcard No. 19
Marvin The Moose

Shortly after we met, Zaheer left on another trip with his parents, to Missouri. They had family there. He was away for two long weeks! It was torture. We tried to stay in touch everyday but it wasn't the same.

The day he arrived back, he presented me with a bag. In the bag was a soft toy, a moose. Around the moose's neck was a beautiful, thin, gold necklace with a small pendant that looked like a bug or a fly. After thanking him profusely, jumping on him and showering him with one thousand kisses, I said, "What a curious looking bug."

He burst out laughing! "It's not a bug. It's an Ashofarohar!"

"A whatohar?"

"An Ashofarohar; the guardian angel Fravashi, from which it gets its name. It's the symbol of Zoroastrianism. It will protect you when I am not there to do that," said Zaheer, romantically.

Oh yes, I forgot to say when I was gushing about him, that he was terribly romantic as well.

Zaheer explained. "It's not only your guardian angel but your guide as well."

While I didn't understand all of that, it was gold, it was unusual and it was from him. I put on the Ashofarohar and never took it off again.

I wore it with pride and loved it almost as much as I loved Marvin — Marvin the Moose from Missouri now went everywhere with us.

Postcard No. 20
From Virgin to Vixen

On my twentieth birthday it happened: we made love for the first time. Stars shot across the skies, bells rang and it was the most amazing feeling ever.

STOOOOOOPPP! Rewind. This isn't a movie!

Making love for the first time was awkward and confusing! I wasn't sure what to do, how to feel, what to hold onto and whether laughing was something I should do the first time. However, we got through it, Zaheer knowing marginally more about lovemaking than I did. However, the third and fourth times started to get more interesting. We now thought we were experts and experimented with various food groups and parts of our bodies. We then started to get very brave and took our sexual activities from under the bedclothes to outside the bedroom. We made love on the kitchen floor, (yes, I know, clichéd stuff) and the bathroom floor (very cold, even in India) and the dining table, the middle of the road at midnight, the backseat of his car, the front seat of his car, the steering wheel of his car and finally, we were swinging from chandeliers and making love on Father's desk in the study. This is significant, as it led to us having to retreat back into the bedroom and under the bedclothes again.

Father and his staff often worked from home and so there was a large study accessible and tempting to us. One night, Zaheer crept into the house and we ventured into the study where there was a lovely, large, felted-oak table. We liked that table as it was nice and warm but the friction wasn't terribly good on the nether regions.

The next day, as Father handed his secretary his diary, there was a pretty, pink, lacy bra, in between the pages. His secretary extricated said bra from the diary and handed it to Father with a straight face, saying, "I think you might want this back, sir," and walked out of the room.

Father stood there with this bra in his hands, completely aghast. He was confused and finally angry, furious that someone would be presumptuous enough to change in his study, never dreaming of the possibility of two lithe, young bodies writhing around on his table.

From that day onwards, he tried to find out in vain who it belonged to, so much so that he was in danger of being done for sexual harassment. He couldn't very well send out a memo asking the owner to collect the item left in his study. Hence, he took it up on himself to play detective. Family, friends and staff alike noticed how he never looked a woman in the face while having a conversation with them anymore: he would stare at her breasts. He was even once caught cupping his hands to try and measure the size of the cleaner's breasts, from the other side of the room.

At meetings, you would see his head and half his body moving slowly to one side to measure up the size of a woman's breasts, if he hadn't seen her before. Finally, I had to tell him it was mine and made up a story of going into the study while I was looking for a pen, with my bra, in my hand as I was about to wear it. Father was so relieved to have got to the bottom of it that he barely questioned me about it.

I was twenty-one and after many tears, pulling out hair, tantrums and sleepless nights, I finally graduated with a

Bachelor of Arts Honours degree in Psychology! We were all elated!

Zaheer was highly intelligent and graduated with very high honours in science. We all got together for a celebratory drink and Mother said to the general, "You must be so proud. He topped his class and graduated with such high honours."

"Yes," said the general, "he did okay, but he only got ninety-eight per cent."

Mother was about to say something like, "How can you possibly expect him to get anything higher?" but caught a glimpse of Father, shaking his head at her. The competition was so stiff in India, that even ninety-eight per cent was sometimes not enough!

It was now time to leave India. Father's stint had come to an end. The thought of leaving Zaheer filled me with dread, anguish and nausea. This was truly the man I was going to spend the rest of life with. I knew that, he knew that, by now my parents knew that and anyone else who would listen knew that.

Mr Raju was the only one who didn't agree or nod acceptingly when I told him. According to him, "One should always marry within one's religion and caste." Mr Raju was quite firm on that. "We do not understand each other unless we are from the same caste. Our ways are different, Charlottie. You should understand that."

"What about love?" I asked Mr Raju.

"*Uska saval hee nahi hota*," said Mr Raju, which meant, 'There is no question of it. The love will come later and if it doesn't come by that time, you are so used to living with that person that you cannot think of living with anyone else'. He was serious.

"I don't think that is a very satisfying way to live," I said.

"Well, Charlottie, these are our ways and we are happy with them. I do not think that divorce is a very satisfying way to live either."

"But what makes you think…?" I was beginning to sound indignant and Mother felt it was time to step in and called out to me to continue packing.

It was decided that as Zaheer was going to be doing his MBA in America — MBAs were an absolutely *must* in those days for an Indian of any standing — he would come and stay with us in the UK over the summer. I was so excited. I was going to see him in two short months.

We packed up all our belongings and left with many more than we had come with. Leaving was most difficult for Dad and me. We had made a home here, had made fast friends here and had bonded with the people and the country.

Mother had 'just visited' physically, emotionally and mentally. She had never felt that she fitted in but then she had never made the effort and she accepted that. Therefore, it was easier for her to leave. She said she would miss the help she'd had and would miss the cook, even though Cook still made spicy dumplings. She would miss the maid even though she still tried to polish all of Mother's silver with tamarind and she would miss Daniel the driver, even though he drove at eighty miles an hour around corners, down a one-way street the wrong way with eleven other modes of transport around him. In fact, I was surprised we were not transporting Mother back in a strait jacket.

She said goodbye to her *theatrelings*. They were all devastated and gave her the leg of a skeleton as a present, to take back with her.

Daniel was in floods of tears. The maids had bundled together all the coloured medicine for Mother to take back and use.

I was leaving the two men in my life who had come to mean so much: Zaheer, who I knew I would be seeing again soon and Mr Raju, that constant presence in my life in India; always there, always caring, looking out for us, entertaining and above all, one of the kindest human beings I would ever meet. He came to see us off the night before in tears. Mrs Raju was in tears and we were told the rest of their family was in tears as well. We took their word for it.

He grabbed hold of Dad and clung to him. Not being the most tactile of people, Father patted him gently on the back and said, "Now, now. There, there, man. Get a hold of yourself."

It took a while for Mother and I to explain to Mr Raju, that he wasn't being obscene and that it was an English expression meaning 'get a grip'. That didn't help, so we just told Mr Raju that Father felt the same way and was expressing it in the way he knew best, with a stiff upper lip.

All three of us were devastated to say goodbye to Rover who was going to stay with the house and be looked after by the maids, till the next occupant arrived.

When we went to say goodbye, he was sleeping in his usual cool spot on the veranda. We hugged him and kissed him and cuddled him with tears in our eyes telling him how much we were going to miss him. He got up from where he was lying down, shook us all off, walked across the room and found another cool spot. We all agreed he would be fine without us.

But as we turned around to go, he got up, came over to Father and put his paw on Father's thigh. Father held his paw in his hand. Rover licked Father's hand and then went back to sleeping in his cool spot.

Clutching Marvin in one hand and feeling for the Ashofarohar around my neck with the other, I boarded the plane with a heavy heart. I waved to Zaheer, the General, Mrs Modi and Mr Raju, who were all standing in the airport terminal trying to look happy. I took one last look at Hyderabad and stepped through the door. As we climbed higher, I looked back at the roads and the traffic. They say if you look back at a place, you will return to it soon. I didn't realise just how soon and under what circumstances.

Postcard No. 21
Back in England

On arriving back home, I immersed myself in getting everything ready for Zaheer's arrival. Everything had to be perfect: where I would take him, what I would show him, friends he would meet, what we would do, where we would go.

It was three days before Zaheer was due to arrive. I could barely contain my excitement and was just leaving the house to do some last-minute shopping, when Father walked into my room with Mother. Father looked like someone had stolen his last bulls eye mint (if you need to ask, you're not old enough!) and Mother looked like she had missed the shoe sale at Harrods.

Dad at home in the middle of the day was strange enough but looking like he did, I knew something must be quite terribly wrong.

"Sit down, Lottie," he said quietly and deliberately, without an apology for the 'Lottie'. Then I knew it was something serious. I sat down.

"It's Zaheer," Father said, "he's had an accident."

I shot up in disbelief.

"Sit down, Lottie," he said.

I sat back down.

"I'm sorry, darling. I am so sorry." At this point, Mother could not hold back any longer and started blubbering like the last pair of shoes in her size at the Harrods sale had been snapped up just before she got to them.

I stood up again and opened my mouth to speak.

Father raised his hand and gestured for me to sit down —
this time I sat down and stayed sitting down because by now
he had tears in his eyes. I had never seen Father cry.

I sat down and he said, "Zaheer is dead."

Postcard No. 22
Can One Really Go Back?

It was a whole year before I could do anything at all. My life almost stood still.

He had been riding his motorbike. He was not going too fast, was wearing his helmet but a tanker had spilt some oil on the road. His bike went into a skid, he couldn't stop it and he skidded and slammed into a tree. The impact was too great and the helmet could not save him.

The moment I heard those words from Father I was in complete denial. I asked Dad if this was the cruellest joke he had ever played on me, and I looked to Mother for reassurance. She was still crying.

"But I just spoke to him last night," I said, my voice trailing off, as I saw Father shake his head again.

"Yes, I know, my darling, but it only happened a few hours ago."

After a while, I picked up the phone and called his number. The General picked up. I always called him 'the General' as he hated it and I loved to annoy him. I could hear sobbing in the background and I hesitated. Surely this was now taking the joke too far.

"Is… is… is it true?"

"Yes," he sobbed. "My beautiful boy has been taken from us. Our lives are over. We have nothing left."

I dropped the phone and don't remember the rest.

Over the next twenty-four hours, I threw up and cried in

equal measures. Marvin was with me, by my side, every step of the way. He never let me out of his sight. He was there to hear me sob, there to comfort me at night and there to just sit and listen to me breathe deeply, as I wasn't doing much talking. I massaged the Ashofarohar so much, that I'm sure some of the gold wore off.

Dad asked me if I wanted to go back to India. At first, I didn't think I could face it. Then I changed my mind. Then I changed my mind again. After four days of packing and unpacking my suitcase and throwing up from the nauseous feeling I carried around with me constantly, I told Dad I had made up my mind and that I had to go. Did he want me to go with him? he wanted to know. "Or I could go with you, darling," Mother said.

"No, I want to go on my own," I told her.

Father said he would get his office to organise one of the guest houses for me to stay in. I shook my head.

"Well, of course, you'll want to stay with the Modis. I'll call them straight away."

I shook my head.

"Who then?" Mother asked.

"I am honoured, Sir," Mr Raju said, when Father told him.

I could not have possibly stayed with the Modis. Mr Raju was the tonic I needed.

I boarded the plane with terrible feelings of dread and doom. But I was comforted by the fact that Marvin had come along with me.

At the best of times, I hated talking to fellow passengers on a plane and having stopped praying a long time ago if you remember, I could only hope the person sitting next to me was typically British and hence would know the British etiquette of flying, which is: one does not talk to one's fellow passengers on a plane, one lifts one's newspaper as far up as possible to block all view of one's face and half of one's body. Once one has established one's personal space, one reads every word of the paper and if one has read the paper, then one pretends to read it again. But the trick is not to ever falter and never let your guard or paper down, to allow your fellow passenger even a split second's chance of smiling at you.

I barely had a chance to practise said etiquette, when a young Indian girl next to me had the audacity to speak.

"Excuse me, but are you going to India?" I looked at her and then looked around, wondering whether I had heard right. The flight was a one-sector flight from London to Hyderabad, so for her to ask that question only reinforced for me how important it was to follow the above flying etiquette.

However, I had been brought up fairly well and so I said, "Yes."

I wish I hadn't though as she then said, "Oh good, so am I."

I thought to myself, *I can't be hearing right*. But I was. The rest of the conversation was as invigorating as the first couple of sentences and I was so thankful when the food came, that I said grace. After the meal, I excused myself and went to spend a penny but ended up spending about ten thousand pounds, given the amount of time I was in there.

When I got back to my seat, she was playing with Marvin. I nearly snatched him off her but politely extricated him from her hands.

"Is he a donkey?" she said. I tried to cover Marvin's ears but it was too late; he had heard already. "No, he's a moose!"

She started laughing, "He's not a mouse."

I covered Marvin's ears even tighter.

"No, a moose," I said. "It's like a stag. You find them in America."

"I've never heard of that animal," she said.

Thankfully, I was then allowed to fall asleep but as I started to wake, I saw her face next to mine, staring at me as I was roused from my sleep due to the landing announcement. She was just about to initiate another riveting conversation when I said to her, "We're coming into land. I must pray."

She gave me a knowing nod and closed her eyes as well but patted my hand intermittently to comfort me.

I disembarked into the comforting arms of Mr Raju who was waiting for me in the arrival's hall and for the first time did not say anything at all. He just put his arms around me, patted me on the back and I knew he understood exactly what I needed: silence and understanding.

Parsees bury their dead very quickly. They believe the soul takes four days to reach its destination and therefore the service had been conducted the day after he died.

'In this supersonic age, no way would it take the soul four days to reach its destination. It might even arrive before it's left!' Zaheer used to joke.

However, there was no body to bury or even to send to the Tower of Silence. Zaheer, even at a young age had always been against that and though his parents were fairly staunch in their beliefs, they had respected his wishes. He wanted any parts of his body that could be used, to be used for other people who needed them: his eyes, liver, kidneys, heart... any part. This was something I had not known and the thought of him spread across many different people made me feel sick and ecstatic at the same time.

Over dinner, Mr Raju and his wife tried to engage me in mundane conversation. However, there was no such thing as 'mundane' with Mr Raju — it was always entertaining or distracting and it was exactly I needed.

Mr Raju had become an avid racing fan and was talking to me about the horse Al Manek. I said I didn't know much about racing but one thing was sure: I didn't recognise the name of that horse. After much discussion and Mr Raju repeating the name of Al Manek several times, he brought me the newspaper to have a look. I read it and said, "Oh, you mean *Almanac*."

"Yes," said Mr Raju, looking confused. "That's what I said. Al Manek!"

That night I couldn't sleep.

At 2 a.m. I looked outside. It was raining hard and I could see the wind was doing battle with the trees and small plants in the garden. The wind was winning and the swing that was tied to a tree with a flimsy rope, had already given up the ghost and was lying in a pool of dirty, muddy water.

Still in my pyjamas, I put on what resembled a raincoat that was lying by the door and sneaked out of the house with Mr Raju's car keys. As I approached the car, I could see through the corner of my eye Mrs Raju watching me through the window upstairs. I could also see she was about to open the window to say something, when I saw Mr Raju appeared and gently put his hand on her arm and shook his head. I opened the door of the car and looked back at the window momentarily. They looked directly at me for a moment and then went back in.

I drove through the wind and rain (you wouldn't expect me to write this scene without it, would you? I suppose I could have said it was a beautiful, starry, moonlit night and that made it all the more poignant. But I am really aiming for dramatic and I think gusts of wind and rain certainly portray drama). Where was I?

oh yes, I drove through the wind and the rain till I finally got to the spot where he died.

His roadside memorial still had fresh flowers near it and I stared at the scene for a while, trying to imagine his last moments, trying to picture him skidding, trying to understand why he couldn't stop himself, wondering what his last thoughts had been, if he did in fact have any last thoughts and asking over and over again, why, why, why? By this time, I was crying uncontrollably

I walked slowly to where he had taken his last breath and lay down in the middle of the road, in the exact same spot where he had lain dead. Soaked in the rain, dirty from the mud on the road and hysterical with emotion, it was there that I felt close to him, that I was able to say goodbye… and there that I accepted what had happened.

The next day, I realised that acceptance was still far away. Mr Raju gently broached the subject of meeting his parents. "They are in shock like you, Charlottie." (Either due to Father calling me Lottie and then trying to change it to Charlotte, or due to the way Mr Raju pronounced all the letters he could see in a word, for one of these reasons he always called me Charlottie. Father could never understand why Mr Raju was allowed to call me that and yet he could not call me Lottie.)

The very thought of seeing his parents made my stomach turn inside out and the little food that was inside, came out. Mr Raju did not mention it again for a few hours, after which he broached the subject again but this time with a towel and bucket to hand. His parents had been asking about me and wanted to know when I was coming to see them.

"I can't, Mr Raju," I said. "I just can't."

"But Charlottie, they are in pain and you are the closest thing to their son."

Self-preservation would not allow me to put my own feelings aside for grieving parents and go to them to give them whatever little comfort they thought they could gain, from seeing me under these circumstances.

They called many times — they who were filled with grief, who were in a state of shock and disbelief, they were calling me and I could not go.

I left India a day later, unable to bring myself to meet them.

"Please, Mr Raju, tell them I love them. I will see them and speak to them but not now and I am very sorry I cannot."

As I boarded the plane, Mr Raju placed a piece of paper in my hand.

"This was the passage read out at his memorial service. Mrs Modi wanted you to have it as you could not be there."

Once I had settled into my seat, I began to read it and when I finished, I managed to get to the toilet just in time to see my breakfast all over again.

It was a passage by Robert N. Test.

'To Remember Me'.

The day will come when my body will lie upon a white sheet neatly tucked under four corners of a mattress located in a hospital; busily occupied with the living and the dying. At a certain moment, a doctor will determine that my brain has ceased to function and that, for all intents and purposes, my life has stopped.

When that happens, do not attempt to instil artificial life into my body by the use of a machine. And don't call this my deathbed. Let it be called the bed of life and let my body be taken from, it to help others lead fuller lives.

Give my sight to the man who has never seen a sunrise, a baby's face or love in the eyes of a woman.

Give my heart to a person whose own heart has caused nothing but endless days of pain.

Give my blood to the teenager who was pulled from the wreckage of his car, so that he might live to see his grandchildren play.

Give my kidneys to the one who depends on a machine to exist from week to week.

Take my bones, every muscle, every fibre and nerve in my body and find a way to make a crippled child walk.

Explore every corner of my brain.

Take my cells, if necessary and let them grow so that, someday a speechless boy will shout at the crack of a bat and a deaf girl will hear the sound of rain against her window.

Burn what is left of me and scatter the ashes to the winds, to help the flowers grow.

If you must bury something, let it be my faults, my weakness and all prejudice against my fellow man.

Give my sins to the devil.

Give my soul to God.

If, by chance, you wish to remember me, do it with a kind deed or word to someone who needs you. If you do all I have asked, I will live forever.

Robert N. Test.

Postcard No. 23
What Do I Do Now?

When I got back, Mother and Father started their whispering again and this time I didn't even try to listen.

Mum: (hand trying to hide her mouth) "We need to do something about her, darling. She's very upset."

Dad: "What do you want us to do?"

Mum: "Let's take her somewhere to cheer her up."

Dad: "What about the zoo? That always cheered her up."

Mum: "Darling, you can't be serious. That was when she was four; she's twenty-one now."

Dad: "Well, darling, she can't have changed that much."

I spent that year trying to involve myself with anything that did not remind me of him and yet everywhere I went, everyone I met and everything I did reminded me of him. I met up with friends that he would never meet, went to places I would never take him to, saw movies he would never know had been made and read news that he would never know had happened. I was worried I would lose the Ashofarohar but couldn't possibly take it off, so formed a terrible habit of touching it every few minutes that made me look like I had a strange, uncontrollable tic. The other thing that reminded me of him the most was Marvin, again constantly by my side. But even though he reminded me of Zaheer, he also brought me great comfort and solace.

During that year everyone tried to help.

Friends suggested I join a gym. I would like to refute a

myth that going to the gym helps you lose weight and keep fit. I went there every day for a month, didn't lose an ounce of weight or get fit. They said, 'Go to the gym, you'll get fit'. So I went and nothing happened. I went, I stood around, then someone said I had to lift something and that was ridiculous - couldn't they see I was lifting my Evian bottle to my mouth all the time and drinking water.

Besides, I hated the gym. I hated the treadmills and the static bikes that went nowhere. I cycled and cycled and all I could see was a horrible TV screen. I didn't actually get to experience the bike ride: I couldn't smell the newly cut grass as I whizzed past the houses and couldn't see the man trying to take his reluctant dog for a walk or feel the breeze on my face.

The General and Mrs Modi wrote to me many times. They sent messages with Mr Raju, tried calling several times in the first year after his death but I could never bring myself to return their calls or letters or requests for a meeting.

My way of dealing with it was to almost forget it ever happened.

Then exactly a year to the day that he died, I couldn't bear to be with anyone but wanted to be with everyone. I didn't want to be with anyone I knew but I didn't want to be on my own. So I literally took to the streets of London and walked and walked and just kept walking till my feet ached but I didn't even feel them.

Then something happened that stopped me in my tracks. I had somehow arrived at Oxford Street. As I was walking past a bus stop, a double decker came to a halt next to me and I saw a young man in a wheelchair trying to get onto a bus. With his hands he had to haul himself onto the floor of the bus, drag his cushion off the wheelchair, then fold his wheelchair up and drag it onto the bus and park it in the right place and then walk on his hands to a seat, onto which he swung himself.

Don't get me wrong, he did all this with the swiftness and sleekness of Cowboy Bill drawing, swirling and shooting his gun. He would have to do that all over again when he got off and who knew how many more times that day. He was probably used to it and thought nothing of it but to me, he came under my 'bravest people in the world' category.

If I was him, would I be that brave? Would I even venture out knowing what I would have to go through to get anywhere? I didn't think I would. Now if he could do that, why was I standing here feeling sorry for myself and what would Zaheer have said? He would have been so disappointed in me.

This man had inspired me so much and my only regret is that I never got the chance to tell him how, in that one brief moment, he had managed to knock me out of my self-pitying state and help me get a hold of my life again.

Postcard No. 24
Up, Up and Away

It was time to decide what to do with myself. For a while I had felt that if I were an astronaut, I could have left this world if only for a short time and surely, that would have helped me to forget about him. (So clearly, I am not yet completely over my self-pitying state!) I thought about hypnosis. At one point I even thought of contacting a medium. But none of these ideas appealed to me completely. Finally, it hit me — I would travel. I would go to all the places that he had wanted to visit. I would experience all the things he had wanted to do. I would do that for him and it would help me come to terms with his death. I would live my life as if I were living it with him. It was the only way I believed I could feel close to him and yet forget him.

However, there was one slight problem. I couldn't do it on my own money so needed someone else's.

I decided the best way to do that was to join an airline and take to the skies as a stewardess. When I told Mother and Father, they were less than pleased, to say the least. This time they did not even try to whisper, nor did they try to cover their mouth with their hands.

Mum: "We can't let her do that, darling. This is just a knee-jerk reaction to (mouthing the words) *what happened a year ago*."

Dad: "Yes, perhaps you're right, darling, but let me talk to her."

I was standing right there and they continued to talk about me like I was in another country.

Mum: "Yes, you do that, darling and make sure she knows how dangerous it is."

Dad: "Oh really, darling! It's not dangerous; it's far safer than driving a car."

Mum: "Really? Tell that to all the poor people who have died in plane crashes or from eating airline food."

Father then turned to me and said, "Lottie, your mother's right; airline food is highly dangerous and the thought of you eating it all the time could be of some concern to your mother and me."

"This is ridiculous," I said. "Talk about clutching at straws. I'm going to join an airline in order to travel. That's what I've decided I want to do with my life — travel."

I eventually got my own way, firstly, because they were unable to stop me and secondly, I promised Mother I would send her a postcard from each destination. They would soon come to be known as the 'Dear Mother' postcards.

For some reason this made her feel I would be safe. The fact that most of the postcards arrived ten days after I had returned or that some of them might have even been sent back to the UK on the same aircraft as me, as cargo in the hold, did not seem to matter to Mum. As long as she got a postcard, she was happy.

Postcard No. 25
Come Fly with Me

Anyone who thinks being cabin crew is easy and that the job is just about being a 'Trolley Dolly', is in for a shock.

Having gone through a rigorous selection process with role plays and group discussions, presentations and interviews, I finally arrived at the first day of my course expecting to be shown how to serve crudités and soup in heavy turbulence.

No such luck.

We were taken to a simulator and told to sit down and buckle up as this was going to be our last flight as a *passenger*. What in god's name were they on about?

Soon we 'took off' and the simulator started to shake and shudder. We were all thrown about in our seats for a bit before we 'crashed': all the lights went off, the whole cabin filled with smoke and the emergency lights flashed, along with a siren that I later learnt was the Evacuation Alarm.

There was screaming and shouting: 'Undo your seat belts. Come this way. Undo your seat belts. Come this way. Jump. Jump.'

It was too realistic *not* to play along. Thus, I completed my last flight as a passenger, as they say you are *never* a passenger again.

During the six-week training course, I learnt how to resuscitate someone in an aisle, how to deliver babies mid-air, how to serve a drink, restrain a passenger, comfort a baby and listen to a passenger complain… all at the same time.

But I also learnt that you start off as a Trolley Dolly, then when you get a bit older you become a Cart Tart and when you are at the end of your career, a senior crew member, you then become a Wagon Dragon. I heard all the usual crew jokes such as —

Passenger to stewardess: 'Where have you been all my life?'

Stewardess to passenger: 'Well, sir, I wasn't born for the first half of it'.

and:

Stewardess on the floor with a torch, searching for something a passenger has lost. Another passenger approaches her and asks her what she's looking for. Still down on her hands and knees she looks up at him and says, 'I'm looking for all the glamour they promised me in the training school'.

It was during my training course that I met Freya. Little did I know what a large part of my life she was to become. We seemed to get on quite well from the start of the course, then one day we both ended up in the loo together. I was washing my hands when I heard her light up in her cubicle.

I said, "I didn't know you smoked? You haven't so far."

She said, "I do, but not cigarettes. I wouldn't touch them with a ten-foot pole." She was puffing on a roll-up of weed in the middle of our training course.

"Freya!" I said, "you know we're banned from drinking alcohol or anything of the sort when training or when we're flying."

"Now," said Freya, "there's one thing you need to know about me: I don't touch alcohol, it's not for me. And I don't smoke; I think it is a disgusting habit. However, weed is something different; it's medicinal." The conversation continued:

Me: "How can you possibly concentrate if you're stoned out of your mind?"

Freya: "Don't be ridiculous! Smoking weed makes it all make sense. How do you think I can make sense of virtually learning a new language when they talk about BCFs and slide packs and NITS and all the other acronyms they have?" (She did have a point.)

Me: "If you get caught, is it worth it?"

Freya: "Weed is always worth it, darling."

Me: "Okay then, let me have a go."

I took one puff and coughed my lungs out and never tried it again.

Freya was the most exquisite-looking girl I'd ever seen. She had tiny, sharp features and was the most petite adult you ever saw. All the male delegates on the course salivated over her but Freya was not in the least bit interested.

"Relationships are for wimps," she used to say. "What is love anyway?"

She was also the coolest, least flappable person I had ever met. *Nothing* moved her, nothing bothered her, nothing annoyed her and nothing ever worried her.

After six weeks' gruelling training, both Freya and I got through and we eagerly awaited to see where our first trips would be: Singapore? New York? Japan?

Nigeria! I was going to Nigeria on my first flight ever.

Freya was off to New York!

"Pah!" she said, when she saw JFK on her roster. "The buildings are too tall." And I believe she meant it.

Life on a Postcard No. 26
I Want to Be Comfortable, Sista — Lagos, Nigeria

Lagos was not widely known as the most exotic location in the world. However, over the years I came to love it and its people. They are humorous, fun-loving people who love life. They are also very rich and usually cleaned out the Duty-Free Bars on every flight.

Dear Mother,

My first flight and I was nervous to say the least, trying to remember how many parts of Bacardi to how many parts whisky make up an Irish coffee. Hang on, is there Bacardi in Irish coffee? I was deep in thought over the recipe of some cocktail or other, when a large Nigerian passenger approached me. She came right up to me, thrust her face as close to mine as humanly possible. "Take me to the sheet house!" she demanded. Not ones to mince their words the Nigerians! But I like that: they are straight-talking and say it like it is. Or sometimes they don't.

"I want to be comfortable, sista," another gentleman said to me and so I brought him another pillow. "No, no, you don't understand, sista," he said. "I want to be *comfortable*." I gave him a quizzical look. "Tcht Tcht," (a sound anyone who has been to Nigeria will be familiar with — it is a way of expressing themselves when trying to get your attention) he said, "you don't understand, sista. I want to *eeeease* myself."

"Whisky with da blocks," (Whisky with ice) was another one I had to get used to.

Finally, the service was over. Half my colleagues went to rest in the crew rest area at the back of the aircraft. I was just about to sit down for the first time, when the same lady who had needed to be taken to the *sheet* house approached me. (She was terribly large, I remember thinking to myself.) This time she said, "I have wet myself." Oh no, I thought to myself, *surely my duties can't extend to cleaning her up*. I gave her some tissues and tried to send her back to her seat.

"No, you don't understand. My waters have broken."

"You've dropped water on yourself?" I enquired. Having heard her clearly the first time, I was hoping I'd misheard her as my brain couldn't take in that this woman was telling me she was about to have a baby at thirty-five thousand feet.

"No," she said. "My waters have broken. You have to help me. I'm in labour."

No wonder she was so large — she was heavily pregnant.

My throat went completely dry and I had difficulty even calling a colleague. But I finally managed to find my voice and called her. *This* cannot *be happening*, I thought, as we laid the woman down in the galley area with blankets beneath her.

My training kicked in straight away. My colleagues brought me all the instruments I needed. I then asked for some towels. They brought them over and asked me what I wanted them for.

"To wipe the perspiration," I said, quite frustrated.

"But she's not perspiring," my colleague said, holding the towel, ready to help.

"Not her! Me! *I'm* perspiring!"

The other passengers commented they could hear a lot of screaming and shouting from the galley area and wondered if everything was going well, as they had been told a woman was in labour. "Yes, she's fine," they were reassured. "All the screaming and shouting you are hearing is coming from our colleague" I'm not quite sure whether that comforted them.

Meanwhile, back in the galley area, the now only half-pregnant, half-delivered lady was telling me to calm down and take deep breaths.

"Breathe, breathe," she said. "And don't worry, sista. This is my third baby."

"Well, that's all very well for you, but this is *my* first!" I said.

In my defence, what I would like to mention is what they do *not* teach you in the training school, is that, along with the lovely baby, wee, poo and lots and lots of blood also comes out from the mother. Finally, after just two hours of labour, the baby was born with the cord around its neck. One of my colleagues helped me to slowly move it over the baby's head and we handed it to the mother.

Then we had to cut the cord. We tied it as per instructions and then I crossed myself three times, said three Hail Marys — not a clue what I was doing; I knew more about cutting cords than Hail Marys — but somehow it seemed to help and I cut it.

There was not a dry eye in that galley and nor was there a dry body. We were covered in fluids of all kinds that I don't care to think about. But the sight of the baby, the face of delight and sheer gratitude from the mother, the cheers from the passengers and the knowledge that, on the first day of my first flight, I had delivered a baby at thirty-five thousand feet, made it all worthwhile.

And no… I would *not* want to do it again!

So as you can see, Mother, you really have nothing to worry about for the rest of my time as a 'flighty': I came, I saw, I delivered.

Wish you had been there.

Love C xxx

And so my travels began with a bang and a squeeze and a birth.

I started dating again and dated many, but stuck with none. That's the funny thing about a person when they die: you only remember the best of them. I didn't get to know the worst of Zaheer and so no one could compete. And though I said I was open to relationships, I was closed to them lasting. 'Nothing was forever,' I would say and the moment I thought I was getting close to someone, I would pull away in case they died.

It was as simple as that: I didn't want to be with them in case they died.

Therefore, my relationships were short-lived and superficial. The travel helped as I didn't have much time to think. I had my dark days when I was alone in my hotel room, perhaps after a crew party when the contents of the mini bar beckoned. But something always told me, getting blind drunk was not the answer.

The answer was out there but I didn't know what it was or when I would find it. So I just waited.

Freya and I were inseparable. We sometimes got the opportunity to fly together but if not, we met at every opportunity. She kept me grounded and made me feel like there was nothing I couldn't face. Nothing fazed her: she laughed in the face of danger, flipped the finger at peril, scoffed at trouble and stayed calm in a crisis — she kept her head, while all around her others were losing theirs. That was why she was so good as cabin crew. And that is why she was so good for me.

There were now occasional phone calls from the General or Mrs Modi and on hearing their voice, I would always put the phone down. I would sometimes dial their number in the hope I would be able to talk but I never waited for them to pick up.

I took to flying like a baby to breast milk. I remember reading an interview about an ex-stewardess, who had started flying in the 1960s. She was asked, "Do you think flying is a job or a career?"

She replied, "It's neither; it's a way of life." And I loved the way of life: the non-routine lifestyle, the travel, and the people I met along the way. I picked up the role fairly quickly and learnt to deal with mishaps well.

Marvin came with me on all my trips and I sent a picture of him to Mother after each flight.

"Why do you keep sending me pictures of that wretched, ghastly, soft toy you carry around with you, Charlotte?" Mother disliked anything childish like that. Marvin liked Mother but Mother didn't like Marvin. Marvin knew that and Marvin didn't care.

Life on a Postcard No. 27
What Happens in The Galley, Stays in The Galley?

Within a few short months of flying, I picked up many hints and tips and useful pieces of information. I learnt that:

• If a plate of first-class food falls on the galley floor, you don't scream, shout or wring your hands in a panic-stricken frenzy. You calmly pick up the meat, the asparagus, the mangetout, the baby new potatoes and you place them back on the plate like you have been taught, with the asparagus exactly at a twenty-degree angle from the logo on the plate. Then you elegantly flick off the fluff from the galley carpet, that has landed on the food like a fine layer of mist on a dewy morning. You then present it to the passenger graciously and with a smile.

• When cooking a lump of meat to medium-rare in the first-class galley ovens, if it falls on the floor, do not try to grab hold of it with your rubber gloves as it will slip out of your hands and you will end up chasing it around the galley. Stick a large fork in it, wipe it off and put it back on the trolley to be carved in front of the passenger.

• When a passenger asks you for something you know for sure you absolutely *do not* have, you *never* say, 'Sorry, we don't have that'. You tell them you will have a look to see if you have it. You go to the economy galley down the back, have a sip of the tea that you brewed earlier, then rush past them to the business-class galley. You then come back and tell the passenger you have looked in the economy- and business-class galleys, but you have one more place to check —the first-class galley — and you hope to find it there. You then rush off again, go in the galley, take a sip of your named water bottle — most crew swig out of water bottles so we name our own, otherwise they become communal water bottles — let a couple of minutes pass and then come back flustered. You apologise profusely to the passenger, saying that you have looked everywhere but just cannot find the item, drink, type of food, etc. that they wanted. They then thank you gratefully for all your trouble. Tick! Another satisfied customer.

• Never drink from a glass. On one of my very first flights, having felt the need for a Coke, I poured one into a glass and was sipping it when a call bell rang. As I was out dealing with the call bell, my colleague who was in the galley was having a sneaky cigarette (although smoking had not been banned at that time, it was not allowed in the galleys where all the food and drink were stored and prepared). As he was enjoying his cigarette, our manager happened to pop into the galley unannounced. He had just enough time to drop his fag into my glass of Coke which was the only body of liquid he could see. The manager could smell the smoke but couldn't see any evidence of it, so started to query whether anyone had been smoking. My colleague said he hadn't seen anyone and they were still in discussion about this when I returned. She asked me whether I had seen anyone smoking in the galley. Although I knew it must have been him, I could honestly tell her I hadn't seen anyone at all. She was still suspicious so continued to sniff around, during which time I picked up my glass and took a huge swig of my drink. As I did so I saw my colleague's face change colour and shape and I soon realised why. The manager continued to sniff around and say, 'I'm sure I could smell smoke when I walked in' and I tried desperately not to swallow my mouthful of cigarette, ash and Coke. She finally left and I projectile-vomited the whole mouthful into the sink. I made him do my drinks service, as well as his own, for the next sector!

Life on a Post card No. 28
The Land of Those Who Are Free

Or in other words, Thailand. When you hear that country mentioned you might conjure up images of long, golden nails, elaborate head dresses and Thai dances. Quite an exotic image and one rich in culture and heritage. However, when you hear the name Bangkok, you might also think of sleazy bars, erotic dancing, strip joints, extremely cheap prostitutes, AIDS and poverty. But that isn't Bangkok, only a part of it.

Dear Mother,

Bangkok, like the rest of Thailand, is extremely rich in culture and heritage but they are well hidden among the extremely busy crowds, dust and building sites that you see down any main street. There are pockets, away from the crowds that serve as a reminder of what Bangkok is really about. It has some of the most famous statues and structures in the world that are often overlooked. Yes, there are girlie bars and cheap shopping (I did some of that) but I couldn't come home, without visiting some of the most beautiful, Buddhist temples you have ever laid eyes on, especially the Golden Buddha Temple.

Hundreds of years ago, when this Buddha image was discovered, it was covered in concrete. One day it fell off its stand and the concrete cracked, revealing the inner layer — gold. It contains over five tons of solid eighteen-carat gold.

I thought I had seen the most awe-inspiring statue of Buddha in the Golden Temple. I was wrong. The Wat Po Temple enshrines the world-famous reclining Buddha. It truly took my breath away. The Buddha lies on a huge slab of stone and is approximately fifty metres long. It is gold-plated, the soles of its feet are inlaid with mother of pearl in an intricately carved design, in the form of one hundred and eight auspicious signs, as the number 108 is very important to the Thai people.

The streets of Bangkok are always crowded, no matter what time of the day or night it was. The expression 'sardines in a tin' came to mind, each time I stepped out. If you are of strong mind and heart, then one of the easiest, cheapest and quickest ways to get to where you want to go is by 'Tuk Tuk'.

However, if you are Austin Powers and 'Danger' is your middle name, then you might like to try one of the motor bike taxis.

You might want to try one of these for the experience but there is no guarantee as to what state you will get to your destination in.

Whatever mode of transport you take, a couple of other places are worth a mention here.

Bangkok is hot, steaming (in every sense of the word!), humid, exciting, busy, noisy, polluted and lively. Thailand is a land of dirt, exquisite temples and grand palaces — a land of fun — it's the Land of the Free.

Wish you were here Mother but I know you are glad you are not.

Love C xxx

Life on a Postcard No. 29
That Difficult Conversation.

My dating continued, still with the most inappropriate suitors: there was the health nut who ate seeds for breakfast, fruit for lunch and raw meat for dinner, the alcoholic who drank beer for breakfast, wine for lunch and whisky for dinner, the recycling nut who insisted we recycle everything, including our used loo paper, as not only was it romantic but saved the environment as well. I was all for saving the environment but the world would just have to die a bit sooner, if I had to use someone's used loo paper.

Mother and Father, , never knew about my relationships as they were all so short-lived.

I tried as much as possible to always have Sunday lunch with them when I was in the country and it was during one of these routine lunches, that they started their eye contact with each other and raising chins again, as if to say, 'You ask her.'

'No, you ask her.'

This time I just chose to ignore it. Finally, Mother gave Father the look that said between clenched teeth — 'Ask her now!'.

Father turned to me and said, "Your mother wants to know if you're having sex with anyone."

"*What*?" I exclaimed. I hadn't been expecting that.

"Darling!" Mother exclaimed but it didn't stop there. Mother's eyes widened and then became slits as she stared daggers at Father.

"No, darling," she said, trying to explain in a nicer manner than the way Dad had blurted it out. "What I was trying to find out was…"

"Your mother wants you to make sure you use a condom," Father interrupted.

"Anthony Baxter!" Mother exclaimed. "For goodness sake!"

"Well, Mum, Dad, at least you're not speaking in riddles anymore, though I'm not sure which I prefer."

"Well, you see, darling," Mother said, "you are still very young and we need to make sure you are being careful and you do hear about these stewardesses getting involved with captains all the time and it does worry me."

"Well, don't worry, Mother, I really haven't taken a shine to flight crew as a whole." "Thank god for that," Mother said. "I hear they have affairs left, right and centre and don't care at all."

"It's not quite as bad as that, Mother but it does go on, as there are so many opportunities."

Father now asked, "Why don't you like flight crew? What's wrong with them?"

"Well Dad, I'm sure some of them are very nice but unfortunately, I must have come across some bad eggs at the start. This then biased my opinion. For example, there was one First Office, who hinted he wanted a one-night stand" (at this point I could see Mother poised with her soup spoon near her mouth, barely able to breathe let alone put the spoon in her mouth), "and when I made it very clear I wasn't interested, he tried to show me what a caring person he was and insisted he always bought his one-night stands breakfast the next morning. Does his generosity know no bounds?"

"However, I don't blame them. A lot of female crew do still want to snag a Captain and so they do throw themselves at them."

"The other day over a drink at the bar, a Captain said to me, 'Do I look like the kind of person girls would go for?' I was trying to think of a polite way of saying, 'Not really', as he wasn't blessed in the looks department but he did my job for me."

"'The answer is no,' he said. 'However, just the other day one of the stewardesses asked if she could sit in the cockpit for landing into Hong Kong, which is a very tricky landing. You have to literally look out for a checked board and then turn right at that board. She thought it was a brilliant landing and how clever I was, she said, to be able to do that.' 'The crew went out for a drink that night and she got very drunk. I helped her back to her room and then retired to my own room. Ten minutes later, there was a knock on my door and she was standing there in her bathrobe, which she threw open to reveal she was completely naked underneath'." By this time, Mother had dropped her spoon in the soup and a bit of it had splattered on her blouse, which she was trying to clean off while listening to me.

"The Captain said, 'I told her to go back to her room as I was a happily married man and quite honestly, I knew she was drunk. Also, I do believe if I hadn't been the Captain, she wouldn't have given me a second glance.' Bless him, he was right, but he is one of the very few to recognize that."

"You see," said Mother, after she had finally composed herself. "This is the kind of thing I'm talking about. All this promiscuity really worries me, Lottie. You really need to be careful."

I reassured her that I wasn't 'having sex' and would let her know as soon as I met someone I was really interested in. "However, it will not be a Captain or a First Officer, of that I'm sure."

Father was still intrigued by this and insisted on an answer as to why I had written them off as a whole group. I think he secretly wished I would hook up with a pilot.

"Well, Dad, I have a theory about male flight crew." Now both of my parents had put down their cutlery and couldn't have been listening more intently, than if I was about to tell them how the Pope had decided to convert to Zoroastrianism. "They meet a lovely vibrant, bubbly, gorgeous stewardess and fall in love, get married and are delighted to show off their arm candy. Then the arm candy has their child and then she has another child and by this time, she's put on a bit of weight, is harassed as she's looking after two children under the age of three, while her flight-crew husband swans off to exotic destinations and she's left on her own half the time, having to manage by herself. So when the flight crew come home, all the wives want to do is hand over the babies and sleep. They aren't arm candy any longer, because they don't have the time or the energy to dress up and look glam and gorgeous. So when the flight crews go on trips, they look at all these lovely, bubbly, gorgeous crew and have an affair with them or they then dump their wives and go after what she used to be. But that arm candy then has a couple of kids and the cycle continues all over again."

"That's my theory anyway and while most flight crew don't do this, there are enough that do and hence they are constantly paying out alimony."

That was my *theory* but it is not a fact, so flight crew,

please don't sue me for libel.

Mother and Father were fascinated.

Mr and Mrs Modi tried to get in touch again, this time through Mr Raju but I wouldn't call them. "Just speak to them one time no, Charlottie," Mr Raju telephoned to say.

"I promise I will, Mr Raju." But I never did.

Life on a Postcard 31
The Crazy Cousin and The Rich Wank... Sorry... Banker.

Soon after I joined the airline, I started receiving letters from Cousin Alicia each time she travelled by plane. It didn't matter that she might not have travelled on the airline I worked for, she still wrote to complain to me about her journey each time. It was like I was her agony aunt of the skies and would be able to feel her pain and understand the difficulties she had just been through. She had married a banker and now lived in Hong Kong, flying all over the world at the drop of a Philip Tracy hat: New York for a friend's thirtieth, Paris for a shopping trip, back to London to see Mamah and Papah, and popping over to Boston, 'just to see the leaves turn colour in autumn. They are so beautiful that time of the year in New England.'.

Each time she flew, there was a different complaint.

This time she had to pop over to Brussels as Tristan, her wank... sorry banker husband, was there on business and she decided to surprise him and therefore needed to buy a ticket at the last minute.

'I got to the airport and first class was full,' she wrote. 'How can so many people have so much money nowadays? Where are they getting it from? When I asked them to take someone off as I'm just not used to travelling in any other cabin, they flatly refused. I couldn't believe it. However, I decided that I really wanted to surprise Tris and therefore conceded defeat and decided to buy a business-class ticket.

Can you believe that to my complete horror they had no seats in business class? I was so determined to go, Lottie —you know what I'm like when I set my mind to something — so I decided to bite the bullet and buy an economy ticket. I crossed myself, folded my hands and looked skywards, wishing Mamah had taught me to pray properly. I sat down in my seat and do you know, Lottie? I could actually touch the person next to me, they were *that* close! The only time I'm used to touching someone on a plane is to tap the arm of the stewardess when I want something.

I was horrified. Is that even legal, Lottie? Is it really legal to carry so many people squashed together in one small space like that? I almost brought it up as an issue for the Hague.'

Life on a Postcard No. 32
Time Travels

It had now been a year since I had been flying and it was time to reassess. I had said I would do it till I "got it out of my system". But I wasn't sure which system and what I was trying to get out of it. I loved the travel and was seeing the world. It was just the tonic I needed. I kept telling myself I must soon decide what I was going to do with the rest of my life and what I really needed to do, was to call the Modis but I didn't do that either… I would do it soon, I told myself.

Life on a Postcard No. 33
So Good They Named It Twice

Dear Mother,

It was my first trip to New York and I was so excited. Freya was on the flight with me and we were arguing about which places to visit first when we got there. There's a lot to see in New York but by the time I got there, I was too exhausted - and here is why....

On the way to New York, we had just settled down to eat our meal after completing the service, when a call bell started to chime incessantly. I was the first on the scene, with Freya hot on my heels. A lady was trying to loosen her son's clothing as he couldn't breathe. I realised he was having some sort of a seizure and suspected it had something to do with his heart. He was eighteen so logic suggested he was too young for a heart attack but I wasn't ruling it out.

Freya went for the medical kit, I called for one of the other crew to help me and we moved him to the floor. When Freya came back with the medical kit, we very quickly tried to get him to bite down on an aspirin tablet. But by this time, he was very agitated, in great pain and spat the tablet out. His condition was worsening every second and there was no time to lose. We moved his mother out of the cabin and one of the crew sat with her and reassured her.

We asked the flight crew to divert to the nearest airport and then we called for a doctor and were delighted we got a response from a lady very quickly. I was about to move aside to let her take over when she said, "What would you like me to do?" I explained the young man's condition and that he might possibly be having a heart attack, but we weren't sure and we had very little time. "You don't understand," she said, "I'm a Doctor of Letters. I can translate *War and Peace* into Latin but I don't know anything about heart attacks."

"While that is an honourable and excellent talent, madam," I said, frustrated through a gritted smile, "I doubt that very much, at this point, it is going to help this passenger, is it?" labouring the point with a large side order of sarcasm.

It was now beginning to get critical and Freya who was helping me, glanced at the doctor's area of the medical kit, the area where no Trolley Dolly dare go! This was full of impressive drugs and syringes to be used *only* if we had a Doctor of Medicine (thought I would stress that) on board. She then looked at me and I knew exactly what she was thinking. In this section was an adrenaline injection, that when rammed into the heart of a person having a heart attack could actually save their life. However, we were not medically trained to know when to administer this or whether the condition was conducive to such a drug.

Our other colleague who was helping us started to get the gist of what we were thinking and when she realisedI had read her mind she shook her head. Just at that point, the passenger stopped spluttering. He was now unconscious. I was now desperate to do everything I could to save his life. We commenced CPR. The flight crew had already started to divert. We were over the Atlantic so it would take approximately an hour to find somewhere. There was no sign of life in this young man. We tried for half an hour with no flicker or sign. Yes, we could have continued with CPR but there was no guarantee. However, the adrenaline, if it worked, could bring him back in a few minutes.

I placed my hand on the syringe. My colleague put her hand over mine and shook her head again. But I wasn't willing to let him lose his life — I simply could not live with myself. "Don't do it, Charlotte," my colleague said. "You could lose your job over this."

"And this young man could lose his life," I said. I looked at Freya. She knew exactly how I felt; she knew I needed to do this, for me, for Zaheer — I needed to risk this, to feel I could at least save one life.

She smiled, nodded and whispered, "Just do it and we'll both go down together. If you don't do it, I will."

I grabbed the needle and without hesitating for a second more, (as I knew had I hesitated even one more second, I might not have done it), I took the injection out and I felt another hand over mine. It was Freya's. With Freya's hand gently resting on mine I rammed the adrenaline needle into his heart. We all held our breath. He didn't move. Nothing. No signs. All of a sudden, he took in a deep breath, spluttered, sat bolt upright and then lay back down again but this time his eyes were open.

He survived and in some small way, I felt while I hadn't been able to prevent Zaheer's death, I had at least been able to save the life of another man who was dearly loved.

We both had to go through a whole disciplinary process and were put through our paces. I was worried; Freya was not. And we managed to keep our jobs. What got me through the process was that I kept telling myself that even if I lost my job, it would have been worth it. Freya got through the process with a steady supply of weed.

I was given a restraining order — I could not go within ten feet of the medical kit.

Love and kisses from your daughter.

xxx

Life on a Postcard No. 34
Quartermaster's Juju

Grandpa Charlie had not been very well and we were all expecting the worst. When I got back from New York, I was told he had gone downhill fast and that I should go and see him before it was too late.

At this point, I don't blame you for thinking there had been nothing in my life except operations, medical situations, death and medical emergencies.

When I got to Grandpa Charlie's house, he was lying on the bed, feeble but alert and holding an old faded photograph. I sat on the bed next to his head and noticed it was a photograph of a young, beautiful Asian girl with lovely, long, thick, black hair.

"Quartermaster's juju," Grandpa Charlie said.

"What?" I said.

I was thankful that insanity was not contagious but worried that it might be hereditary. Then I realised he must be hallucinating. "When I was in Burma," he started — Grandpa Charlie had been in the Second World War as a Battery Quartermaster Sergeant in the 42nd Division.

"When I was in Burma," he repeated, almost like he was waiting for me to mentally process the image, "we had finished our act of service and were about to move to Rangoon. I saw an old lady scrounging around for leftover bits and pieces to eat. We had more than enough food to get us to Rangoon, where we would pick up more supplies, so I took the excess, called the head man of the village and told him to tell the old lady not to worry, as I was sending food for her and the rest of the villagers.

"Just before we left, the head man came to see me and said, "The old lady wants you to come to the village so she can thank you." I followed him to her hut. She came out with folded hands and her head bowed. She thanked me in her pigeon English and called to someone inside the hut. From the hut, emerged one of the most beautiful girls I had ever seen. She was the old lady's granddaughter and had the longest, thickest and blackest hair with eyes the size of dark, full moons."

"The old lady indicated to me that in return for all the food, she would like me to have the pleasure of her granddaughter's company. Being an officer and a gentleman, I thanked her, but refused, saying it was not necessary."

"I said it was getting late and we had to leave. The granddaughter started to cry. She asked me to wait. She went into the hut and was there for a while. I started to say goodbye to the other villagers when the grandmother emerged and said, "Please wait as my granddaughter wants to give you something."

"The girl came out of the hut and there in her outstretched arms, was all her lovely, long, black hair. "She has cut off her hair as a symbol of her gratitude for you. She will not associate with another man till her hair has grown to the same length again."

"I was speechless. I knew how important hair was to a Burmese woman. It was a symbol of beauty, vanity and even dignity. They never cut their hair."

"I carried the hair back to the camp and showed it to all

the West-African soldiers, who also knew the significance of the hair. They passed it around slowly, looking at it, feeling it, marvelling at its symbolism. Then one of them held the hair in both his hands and raised it above his head so that everyone could see it and he shouted, "Quartermaster's juju!" A juju was the most powerful accessory to a West-African soldier. It was something that symbolised their power, their 'mojo'. Many of them had black threads tied around their arms, with a little container attached to it in which they kept their juju."

"Quartermaster's juju!" he repeated, and a roar went up from the crowd. "Quartermaster's juju!" he yelled and the roar was deafening this time."

"I carried my juju with me for many days. It smelt of lovely, sweet oil and I wrapped it in a towel in an attempt to keep the sweet smell alive. Eventually, when I could carry it with me no longer, I took it to the forest (she had been born in a forest) and I put a match to it and watched it burn and smelt the sweet smell it emitted, as the flames from it rose higher and higher."

"Today, even though I don't have my juju, I can still feel the power."

A day later Grandpa Charlie died and I repeated that story at his funeral. There was not a dry eye in the house. More power to Grandpa Charlie, as I knew his juju was with him still.

My next trip after Grandpa Charlie died was Delhi.

Life on a Postcard No. 35
Coke and Peanuts

Dear Mother,

I was very excited as I never went to Delhi when we lived in India. I told the crew I could speak a bit of Hindi so I could translate for them and that I was well-versed in the Indian culture. However, what I wasn't prepared for was…

When out with the first drinks round, I was asked by the first passenger for 'cock and penis'.

The gentleman next to him said, "Yes, I will have cock and penis as well; me too, cock and penis."

Soon, the whole row was asking me for cock and penis.

I looked quizzically at my colleague. She smirked and said, "Well, Charlotte, you said you spoke the lingo and could translate for us, so please, do translate." I lifted my hands up as if to say, 'I give up'.

I was then duly informed by my colleagues they were asking for 'Coke and peanuts'.

After the service was over, I walked down the aisle and a lady stopped me to say the gentleman next to her did not speak any English and she thought he wanted something. So, I spoke to him in my broken Hindi and ascertained he wanted some water. I brought it to him and then said, "The next time you want water, don't wait for me to come through the cabin, just press here," (and I showed him the call bell). The next time I went down the aisle I saw him pressing the call bell incessantly with his glass underneath wondering why the water wasn't coming out.

The pièce de résistance was another gentleman, who grabbed me as I went down the aisle. He pointed to the call bell, which apparently, he had been pressing continually but getting no response. He said, "I have been fingering you from that time and still you have not come!"

It brought back all the memories of Hyderabad and Mr Malapropos.

Much love,

C xxx

Life on a Postcard No. 36
Where Is He?

Shortly after arriving back from Delhi, I went to the supermarket to do my three-day shop for food, as that was the length of time I had in the country before jetting off again. Obviously, Marvin accompanied me. Halfway through the shop I couldn't find him. He had clearly jumped from my trolley and wandered off

After tearing down every aisle I had been in, I ran to the nearest employee and in a panic-stricken voice yelled, "I've lost Marvin!"

She calmed me down and in a very reassuring voice said, "Don't worry, madam, we're used to this sort of thing. You go down the middle, I'll go to the left and my colleague will go to the right and we will converge in the middle at the front. We'll find him. There's only one way out of this store."

All three of us flew around the store shouting "'Marvin! Marvin!" Finally, I saw him at the cake counter eyeing up the cream horns.

I shouted to the ladies, "I've found him!" They rushed over to me with great joy on their faces, till they saw Marvin. Then their faces fell and one of them opened her mouth to speak but the other put her hand gently on the other's arm and they walked off, both glancing back at me, shaking their heads.

A week after I arrived back from Delhi, I received yet another letter from Mrs Modi asking me to call or just write to her. She had heard through Mr Raju that I had called him from

Delhi. Why had I not called her?

I must contact her, I would say to myself as I did each time and I put the letter away.

I decided to ask Freya what she thought and why she thought I was avoiding them. When we met for our weekly dinner, I told her they had tried contacting me again and what did she think.

Freya: "Do you want to contact them?"

Me: "Yes and no."

Freya: "Yes or no?"

Me: "Well, I really can't bring myself to do it as I feel I've managed to move on and don't want to take myself back there again."

Freya: "You have not moved on. You will never move on. They will never move on. You all have to deal with it in the best possible way. You're not contacting them because you don't want to feel the pain again; they are contacting you because they want their pain eased."

Even for Freya, this was insightful but it wasn't the answer I wanted to hear. I had wanted her to say, 'No, you don't need to contact them. You can put this behind you now and move on. Contacting them will only make it worse for you and you have to protect yourself'.

But she didn't and the very annoying thing about Freya was, that she never told you what you wanted to hear. She only told you the truth and sometimes the truth was bloody painful. So I decided she was wrong.

"By the way," she said. "I've met someone and he's joining us tonight."

Me: "*What*? You waited this long to tell me?"

Freya: "Well, you were whingeing and moaning about

should I contact them or shouldn't I and I didn't want to interrupt."

Me: "When and where did you meet him? What's he like? How long has it been? Why didn't you call and tell me?"

Freya: "Last week, in a bar. Hmmm nice enough, been a week, wanted to surprise you."

Me: "But I can't believe…"

I didn't have time to finish my sentence because there, in front of us, was standing one of the hunkiest creatures I had ever seen!

Freya gave him a cursory glance, made room for him and casually introduced us: "Charlotte, Adrian. Adrian, Charlotte."

"Wow!" I said. "Freya only just told me about the two of you. How lovely!"

"Yes," Adrian gushed. "I was lucky enough to be heading towards the gents when Freya was coming out of the ladies and we literally bumped into each other. I couldn't believe my luck when I asked her out and she said yes, although I think her exact words were, "Well, I suppose so"."

"That's Freya for you," I said.

Adrian was charming, funny and witty. He was an animator and specialised in what he called the *Jungle Book* era of animation, where everything was done by hand. "Not like the computer-generated stuff these days."

As he was a dying breed, he was in great demand. This didn't impress Freya one little bit. Come to think of it, not much impressed Freya. Adrian was so in love with Freya but she treated him like an annoying fly on her sleeve. I couldn't understand it.

Life on a Postcard No. 37
The Retiree

Life carried on as normal and then, just before I was due to go on my next trip, I was summoned to Chez Baxter.

"Well, darling, we have some wonderful news!" Mother enthused. "You tell her, darling." She nudged Father on his shoulder.

"No, darling, I think you should tell her," Father said, graciously.

I could tell Mother was about to burst and I wanted to delay her agony a bit longer so I said, "Let me guess… you're pregnant."

Mum: "Now, Lottie dear, what kind of a guess is that?"

Me: "I was adopted?"

Dad: "No, Charlotte. Don't be silly."

Me: "The lawn has finally been mowed."

Mum: "Lottie!"

Me: "You're giving up your life here and going on a world tour."

They both stopped and looked at me.

Me: "That can't be it! You can't be serious!"

Mum: "Well not exactly, darling but your dad has decided to take early retirement and we do want to travel but we want to travel with *you*! Isn't that wonderful?"

I felt the blood drain from my brain and the room started to spin. I grabbed the nearest thing I could hold onto, which was an armchair and managed to sit down without passing out.

My parents were very confused by my reaction and started to talk to each other again but this time, it didn't annoy me as I was desperately trying to remain conscious.

Mum: "What's wrong with her, darling?"

Dad: "I'm not sure. It could be a coincidence that she felt faint at the point we told her I was retiring."

Mum: "It might be that she's so excited she had to sit down."

Dad: "I don't think one reacts like this when one is that excited."

Mum: "Well, I saw a programme once where this lady was given a cheque for one million pounds and she passed out. It could be that kind of excitement."

Dad: "I don't think so somehow, darling. Do you think she needs some water?"

Mum: "That's a good idea. I'll go and get some."

With that, Mother filled a glass of water and brought it to me which was the best thing she could have done, as by now my throat was completely parched. Mum walked towards me with the glass and just as I was reaching for it, she threw it in my face.

I started spluttering and choaking.

Dad: "What did you do that for?"

Mum: "Well, I'm sure Lottie told us this is how to deal with someone who feels faint."

Me: (*splutter, splutter, cough, cough*) "No, Mum, that was not it. I said put their head between their legs, with their head lower than the heart. That's how you stop someone passing out! There was no mention of water in the face!"

Mum: "Sorry, darling but at least it has brought you round

again."

After reassuring them I was okay and that I was delighted for Dad and of course would love to have them come on a *few* of my trips, I left and got in my car, hoping I could stop myself from driving it into the nearest tree.

Introducing my parents to friends was hard enough; letting them spend any amount of time with my friends was almost unthinkable without Valium. So now, having to take them on trips where they would practically spend days with people I actually knew, was making me quite nauseous and for the first time in my life, I considered hard drugs. This needed some thought and I needed lots of time to give it lots of thought.

Life on a Postcard No. 38
The Fragrant Harbour

In Cantonese, 'Heung Gong' (the words for 'Hong Kong') mean 'Fragrant Harbour', which had been the original name of this precolonial fishing port. This area was also known for producing incense, hence the name. Though the harbour is no longer fragrant, that does not take away the beauty of Hong Kong.

Dear Mother,

Absolutely loved Hong Kong!

As I peered out of my hotel window, I could see old rundown buildings ready to drop and beyond that I could see the harbour with the Star Ferry going back and forth to Kowloon. I could also see some expensive yachts next to local junks and fishing boats, all glistening in the Hong Kong sun. In contrast to the old rundown buildings, I could see state-of-the-art skyscrapers crowding each other's space and beyond, mountains whose peaks disappeared among the clouds. They looked almost unreachable past the concrete jungle that Hong Kong had now become.

Roaming the streets at night, jet-lagged was the most surreal experience. Hong Kong like New York, never sleeps. With lights from adverts and buildings blazing through the night, you can wander the streets at any time and feel like you are in a squash court, with the spotlight on you at all times.

It's a fascinating place, Mum.

The island's advertising slogan is: 'Hong Kong — Stay another Day'.

Believe me, you will want to.

Life on a Postcard No. 39
Only Vanilla?

Shortly after I returned from Hong Kong, I had another letter from Cousin Alicia. Her children's nanny's mother had died and she needed a few days off.

"Can you believe how inconvenient that is for me, Lottie? Who's going to look after my children? I don't think she really cares Lottie. However, I'm back in Hong Kong now and sorry I missed you. I was in good ol' Blighty when you were in Hong Kong! Such a shame you weren't well enough to look up Tris and that you had an upset tummy when you arrived here. What jolly good luck it got better the day you were leaving. He would have loved to have met you. However, let me tell you about the horrors of my flight over to England…"

She had been travelling with her youngest: four-year-old Olivia, who was an absolute darling (clearly adopted). She also had two boys: an eight-year-old Rupert and a six-year-old Hugo; both terrors and not to be underestimated (clearly her own children).

"I thought I must share with you this journey that has been so harrowing and full of hardships. Having secured our 1E and F seats and after a visit from the Captain, when he saw the kids, gifting them with some postcards and telling them they were sitting just behind him, I was confident we were in for a passable journey. Oh boy, was I wrong?"

"Firstly, it was a 767. Need I say any more? Clearly not, but do bear with me as I go on."

"So there I was, sitting in my seat and was handed the menu."

"The first challenge of the flight: the agonising decision whether to choose the smoked salmon starter or the caviar starter. I looked around but there was no one to help me. I had to do this on my own. I'm afraid it was too difficult. I ordered both, stating, 'Yes of course my four-year-old child eats caviar and I love smoked salmon'. Once that was over, I had barely composed myself when I had to choose the main course. I cannot even begin to tell you the feelings of deprivation that came over me, when they told me there was no chicken Kiev left. This meant I had only four other choices. Have you ever tried to choose from only four choices? If this was not hardship then I really don't know what is. (What was that you said Lottie? What difference did that make as I am vegetarian?) How could you! What has that got to do with anything! It is the principal of the matter."

"I finally chose a vegetarian option and some Thai noodles for Olivia. I was so incensed from that lack of choice, that I refused to choose any dessert and concerned I was not having my fair share of fat and cream to fill my arteries, they offered me ice cream. Now this is where I must ask you to brace yourself. If you are not sitting down, do so. Make sure you are holding onto something, as this will not make for pleasant reading. The most horrendous hardship of the flight came when they offered me an ice cream. I know this is going to sound too unbelievable to be true but it is true."

"Excitedly, I looked at the tray of ice cream. My blood went cold. I felt faint. There was only one choice. But that was not the worst of it — The only choice was vanilla! Yes, just VANILLA!"

"I didn't remember anything after that. The next thing I felt when I came round, was an oxygen mask being shoved into my face and I saw the anxious faces of the crew. After two and a half bottles of oxygen on one hundred and twenty litres a minute, they managed to get some colour back into my face."

"I apologised and explained that when one is used to eating Elderflower ice cream with a hint of mother of pearl and diamond shavings, then surely they could understand my condition. They mumbled something about cutbacks and the flight continued as if nothing had happened."

"When this horrendous experience was over and we finally landed, we had to disembark with other passengers because the Economy passenger jetty was not working. I don't know why that surprised me. I tried my level best not to touch any of them but just kept comforting myself, that I could always be fumigated upon arrival Chez Smythe."

"I was so thrilled at being able to fall into the outstretched arms of Mamah and Papah and the reassuring hello of our chauffeur, that I never thought things could get worse. As I pushed the trolley towards said chauffeur and told him to 'Put the bags in the back', he started to lift one of them, (yes of course they were heavy — you know my jewellery itself takes up a whole case's allowance) and he promptly collapsed under the weight. But not only that, he collapsed right in front of me. Can you believe I actually had to step over him, Lottie? I don't know how many times I must have told him that if he absolutely *must* collapse, he should do so to the left of me or to the right of me. Left or right, I have no preference but *not* in front of me. It's so annoying when one has to walk *over* him to get to the car."

"The whole experience has been devastating and painful."

Life on a Postcard No. 40
The Bermuda Triangle

Father had retired and now my parents were poised to come with me on *all* my flights! The horror of this hadn't had time to sink in, when they badgered me to take them on my next flight. I begged Freya to come with me and to bring her weed. She said she loved me but even weed wouldn't be enough; but she would be with me in spirit. That gave me a good idea. Perhaps if I drank enough alcohol, that might just dull the pain.

They got on board and Mother was super excited. Father was nonchalant but I could see how proud he was to see me going about my work. On boarding, Mum came up to me to give me a big hug. "No, Mum, other passengers really don't need to know we're related."

As I went down the aisle, she would occasionally whisper, "Oh, darling, are you sure I can't help you? You look like you've got a lot on the trolley there. Shall I take some things back for you to the galley?" (She'd learnt all the terms.)

"No, Mum," I said through gritted teeth. "Why don't you relax and enjoy the flight and let me get on with my work."

Dad had been to Bermuda before and said he was going to look up an old friend when he got there.

When we got to the hotel, Mother couldn't contain her excitement. She was also curious about the crew. She whispered again to me, as we were waiting to get our rooms, "Are any of them sleeping with the Captain this time?"

"Mother! Please!"

The next day, we had arranged to go swimming with dolphins. It was a crew thing: we couldn't leave Bermuda without swimming with dolphins. When Dad heard about Dolphin Quest in Bermuda, where you just got into the pool, as it were and swam with them, he said, "Charlotte, that's outrageous. How can they treat dolphins this way? That's no way to swim with dolphins."

After making a few phone calls he came up to the room very excited. "Be ready in your swimming gear at 4 a.m. tomorrow. We are going to actually swim with dolphins!"

It was all very cloak and dagger. We met Father's *friend*, who Mother had never met and was an ex-colleague of his from way back. We drove an hour in his car, in pitch darkness and mostly in silence, till we came to a very secluded beach. Well, I guess at 5 a.m. it would be secluded, unless you were deranged fools like us. I hadn't even known Bermuda was long or wide enough to drive for an hour. We finally got out and Father's friend looked around, making sure we weren't being observed.

"You must understand that what we are doing is kind of… sort of, almost… well nearly… illegal."

Mother didn't look shocked or surprised or even worried. She asked, very matter of factly, "Well, is it or is it not illegal, what we are about to do?"

"Best you don't know, darling. The less you know, the less you can confess to if we get caught," Father said, with a smirk.

"Let's just say we shouldn't really be doing this, as these are uncharted and unregulated waters and we shouldn't be taking a boat out or swimming anywhere near here," his friend said.

We took our clothes off, underneath which we had our

wetsuits and got into his motor boat. It hummed softly as we meandered to the middle of what I think, was still the Atlantic Ocean.

Then Father's friend stopped his boat. He looked into the distance through his binoculars, pursed his lips and said, "Just as I thought. Bang on the money. Right every time. Never fails. So predictable these dolphins are."

He started the boat again and all three of us strained our eyes to see what he was talking about. Shortly, he shut off the engine. The boat drifted for a bit and then he put the anchor down.

"What now?" Father said.

"Now we wait," said the friend.

We waited for what seemed like a century, straining our eyes and our ears, all our senses heightened and alert.

We heard a splash. We looked around but could see nothing. Then all of a sudden, there was another splash on the other side of the boat. Again, we looked but could see nothing.

The friend said, "Get in." We all hesitated. "Get in," he said, gesturing with his chin towards the last splash.

We let ourselves into the water gently, still clinging onto the boat. "Don't be scared," he said. "Just swim a bit. They'll come to you."

"Are… are… you sure about this?" Mother said.

Just as she said that, we heard a splash followed by the sight of a tail. You could not mistake the dolphin's tail. I let out a gasp. I didn't hesitate for a second after that. I swam as fast as I could towards the tail and the splashing. I couldn't ever remember being so emotional or excited. I half-expected the splashing to stop or to get more furious as the dolphin swam away from me.

Mother shouted after me, "Be careful Lott—" But I didn't even hear her because before she could finish her sentence, out of the water, barely a foot away from me, rose one of the most magnificent sights I had ever seen. The dolphin rose up out of the water, squeaking and screeching. When you ever hear the expression 'Burst into tears', you don't really truly know that that means till it happens to you.

"He's taken a shine to you," said the friend. "Just wait there. He's figuring you out."

The dolphin swam around me. I put my hand out and he came closer but not close enough for me to touch him. He then withdrew and went towards Father and circled round him. He came back to me and then went towards Mother.

"Now I don't have any food," she said to the dolphin quickly, out of nervousness. Both Father and I burst out laughing. The dolphin went under the water and so did I. I could hear him squeaking again and before I knew it, there was another one by my side. At this point, any concern I had left me and I tried to touch the second one. This time it let me. We swam with them for ages. What amazed me the most, was that they didn't get bored of swimming with us and it felt like they were enjoying it as much as we were.

Finally, as dawn broke, the friend said conspiratorially, "We must go. We mustn't be seen here."

Reluctantly, we got back into the boat after bidding the dolphins goodbye. They swam around the boat as we got into it. The friend looked around again to make sure there was no one about, then he threw something into the water which the dolphins dived for and ate.

"What was that?" I asked.

"Dolphin food. I'm not supposed to feed them," said the

friend with a smile, "but they love it, so I usually bring them a snack."

As we started the quiet engine, we saw ripples on either side of the boat. As we watched, the dolphins leapt out of the water on either side of the boat, crossed over each other, over our heads and dived back in again. We looked at each other open-mouthed. Dads friend said, "Aaah that's nice. They're saying goodbye."

Now *that's* what I call swimming with dolphins.

As an aside…

Soon after the supermarket incident with Marvin, I started to have some strange dreams about him. I dreamt that he was Marvin the Moose from Missouri and he had come to England, to live with a man called Simon the Human. The dreams were fleeting to begin with but then started to get very strange and realistic. This one was about Marvin going to the supermarket.

It was the weirdest and most vivid dream I had ever had but put it down to the fact, that I nearly lost him in the supermarket and that this was just transference of my anxiety.

I decided to tell Freya about my dreams. "They're quite natural," Freya said. "You have a vivid imagination and vivid imaginations give rise to vivid dreams."

I wondered why I ever told her about them because to Freya, everything was natural. You could grow a courgette on your head and she wouldn't bat an eyelid.

"I have dreams like that all the time," she continued.

"Yes, but that's because you're stoned out of your mind most of the time," I said.

Life on a Postcard No. 41
Best Snog I Have Ever Had: Lusaka, Zambia

Dear Mother,

I can't tell you how elated I am being here. You know my love, passion and obsession with animals and so you can imagine what kind of paradise I was in when I went on safari down the Luangua River. It has been one of the most exhilarating experiences of my life! At the safari camp, we slept in tents outdoors and could hear the animals all around us. Each day we would wake at 4 a.m. and go out for our morning safari, just as the animals were getting up for breakfast. The first day I was barely a few metres away from a lion cub. He just sat there on the rocks and looked at us. A few feet away from him were his parents, who waited patiently while we clicked our cameras and then, when they felt we had enough time ogling their child, the father slowly got up from where he was sitting.

Just the gesture of him standing up and ambling over to us, with his mane flapping in the breeze, was enough to put the fear of God into us. He looked so majestic and magnificent and even though I was gripped with fear, my first instinct was to run over and embrace him.

That night, once the camp was asleep, I sneaked out to sit by the riverbank. It was pitch dark as all the lights had been turned off, so as not to scare any animals. I had been told by the guide that hippos come to the banks at night and communicated with each other. Soon enough, I heard them.

They sounded like old ladies laughing.

I listened, fascinated, feeling slightly apprehensive as the guide had warned us not to venture from our tents because even though hippos were herbivores, they wouldn't hesitate to break us in half if they felt we were a threat to them.

Suddenly, I heard a squishing noise behind me. I walked towards it and heard it move away. I moved towards it. This carried on for a few minutes till there was a clearing in the bushes. I turned the corner and came face to face with the largest hippopotamus I had ever seen in my life. He opened his mouth and let out a roar, loud enough to shatter the glass on the car carrying the United States President. I ran back to the camp into the arms of a very angry guide, who threatened to send me back to the city if there was a repeat performance such as this. I promised him that after this I would be as obedient as ever... until temptation presented itself, yet again.

The next day we went on a horseback safari. We were told that some of the giraffes would approach the horses as they did not see them as a threat and if we wanted to, in order to get better pictures, we could give them a certain feed they provided for us, which were some sort of pellets that were nutritious for them. Having never felt any fear of any animal, I decided to hold back as the others trotted on ahead. I wanted to see how close I could actually get to these gigantic, graceful creatures. Sure enough, they approached the horses with little caution and I threw the feed to them, which they ate and they then came closer, so I could get the obligatory 'great photographs'.

But that was not enough for me: I wanted a close encounter of my own kind.

I stopped my horse and held out my hand. One of the

giraffes approached me with caution. He came close but did not take it. I threw the food down very close to me. He picked it up. Another giraffe saw him do this and came around the other side. I held out my hand again and maybe trying to outdo his mate, or the desire for the feed was too great, he took it from my hand. I was thrilled. How can I get them to come closer I thought to myself. (Okay Mother, stop biting your nails, I promise this does have a happy ending.)

This time I put my hand very close to my chest and he again came closer, more hesitant than the first time but gently and slowly he took the feed from my hand. As he did so, his long, black tongue scratched the surface of my palm. The feeling was indescribable. The thrill of seeing this giant bend down really close to me with the biggest eyes and eyelashes, was too tempting for me to stop there! I had to have more!

This time, with little hesitation, I put the feed between my lips, making sure I held it lightly. I then stuck my face out as far as I could.

He saw it, he hesitated, he walked away. A second later, he turned and came back. He stopped, then as if in slow motion, he bent down, his huge face coming towards mine, his eyes the most beautiful, brown pools, his eyelashes flickering in the breeze and with the longest and roughest, black tongue I have ever seen, he gently took the feed from my lips.

I was only able to do this once more before I was noticed as missing. There was no one to take photographs of this event, no one to witness it. I didn't need that. The image of that face near mine did not need to be captured by a camera. It was with me forever.

SOMEONE GET MOTHER THE SMELLING SALTS PLEASE! MOTHER! Are you okay!?

Love C

xxx

On returning from Lusaka, I was on a high. I wished I could have shared this experience with Zaheer. He would have loved it. But he wasn't there. So, who better then to share it with than his parents? I picked up the phone. Bizarrely, my fingers were shaking as I dialled their number. I heard a click on the end of the line and barely waited for the 'Hel—' before something inside me forced me to put the phone down. No sooner had I done that, than they rang back. I switched my phone off and did not try that again.

My almost weekly dinners with Freya continued. Sometimes, Adrian would join us and was always amazing company and I often mentioned to Freya how lucky she was. "Phaa!" she would say. "He's okay."

This time he wasn't with her.

She plonked herself down in the chair and declared, "I think I need to dump Adrian."

Me: "What? Why? Isn't he gorgeous?"

Freya: "Yes, I guess."

Me: "Isn't he loving and caring?"

Freya: "Guess so."

Me: "Isn't he witty and funny?"

Freya: "I suppose so."

Me: "Isn't he romantic?"

Freya: "Suppose so."

Me: "Isn't he thoughtful?"

Freya: "S'pose so."

Me: "Then why?"

Freya: "He keeps sending me corny jokes. Look at these."

There were some roadworks being carried out on the pavement. It made me cross.

The other day I was at the post office and a crazy man threw some eggs, milk and cheese at me. How dairy.

I am so upset my pet mouse Elvis died. He was caught in a trap.

Me: "Yup, you're right. Dump him!"

Life on a Postcard No. 42
Fag Hag

Even though Adrian tried very hard to bring along a fourth each time we met, my mind seemed to be closed to meeting anyone. My dating stopped for a while and I became a fag hag.

Being part of an airline where over fifty per cent of the crew were gay, it would have been rude not to. It was at this point I met Graham — or 'Gayem' as I called him — the greatest drama queen that ever minced the earth. Now you would think that with all my trips and flights and experiences, the *last* thing I would need in my life was drama, but Gayem was addictive. Once I'd met him, I had to get more of him.

I met him on a flight to Houston, when a Texan ranch owner didn't think there was anything wrong with bringing a live snake on board, hidden in his cabin bag. Yes, I know what you are thinking: she's making this up as the snake would have never got past Security unless it had its own passport, ESTA visa and a first-class boarding card. However, we're talking pre-2000, so you have to take a leap of faith and accept that this could happen. And it did.

Unfortunately, the Texan fell asleep and the snake, feeling slightly peckish, managed to get out and headed straight for another passenger's chocolate brownie. All hell broke loose and Gayem was right in the middle of it. He shrieked, screamed and flapped his hands about and pranced around, fanning his face with his hands.

He then grabbed hold of a first-class cloth napkin and started trying to get the snake away from the passenger, who was sitting so still I thought rigor mortis had set in. With each flap of the napkin and '*shoo*', Gayem got louder and louder and shriller and shriller till finally, the Texan must have woken up and realised what had happened. He charged down the aisle, grabbed hold of the snake and put him back in his bag.

I asked the gentleman to follow me to a secluded area of the plane, gave him a stern talking to, all the time bearing in mind he had a live snake in his bag. I isolated him in a remote seat and went to check on Gayem.

By this time, he had thrown himself into the flight deck, hyperventilating and trying to explain the situation to the flight crew at the same time. When they looked like they could do with a translator, I stepped in and explained the situation to them. They, in turn, informed Houston that we had a snake on board. Yes, of course I wouldn't disappoint you: they rang through and said, "Er, Houston... we have a problem."

I calmed Gayem down by showing him images of Judy Garland, a rainbow and Barbra Streisand. When we landed, we expected to see the equivalent of the RSPCA or a representative of a wildlife sanctuary with a lovely cage, ready to whisk the snake off to a happy and free life in the wild. But when the aircraft doors opened, we were met with three policemen and a pair of handcuffs. "Where is it, ma'am?" one of them said to me, in his broad Texan accent.

"Well, wherever it is, officer, I doubt you'll be able to get a pair of those on it," I joked.

Without a hint of a smile or a glint in his eye, he said, "You leave that up to us ma'am, You're in the United States now." They walked down the aisle, giving Gayem a sideways glance as he breathed in and out of a paper bag.

Suffice to say, they never did get those cuffs on the snake as they were for the rancher but I was glad I was not in the Texan's shoes, as those policemen had no sense of humour. As he was escorted off the plane, it saddened me to think he would not be able to get any mileage at all out of this, as it would fall on deaf ears and get no laughs at all.

"No, officer, I promise, that is not a snake down my trousers. I'm just happy to see you."

"I promise you, officer, it is only my one-eyed, purple, trouser, yoghurt monster."

"I had no choice, officer. If you had a snake that big what would *you* do with it?"

After that hugely bonding experience, Gayem and I were virtually inseparable. He was my gay husband and we had an amazing marriage. Gayem never failed to make a drama out of nothing and yet he was the most unsympathetic, gay man I had ever met. I, of course, introduced him to Freya and she was as calm as he was hysterical. They got on well, as long as Gayem didn't annoy her too much. She would often give him 'that look', which almost turned him to stone; a combination of the look a mother gives a child that is getting too hyper or that a wife gives to her husband when she thinks he is being silly.

Life on a Postcard No. 43
Jamaica, Maaaann

Dear Mother,

My flight to Kingston, Jamaica, has been the oddest one to date.

Halfway through the flight, the captain called down to say he had a warning on his panel about Door Three Left…

The warning light indicated that the door lock had been tampered with and although the door wouldn't fly open as we were pressurised, it would start to get dangerous once we depressurised. If the door lock wasn't functioning, then someone would have to stand by the door constantly to make sure it didn't open when we started to descend.

On checking the door, nothing seemed amiss. I reset it as we would normally do but an hour later it happened again, so I reset it again. When it happened a third time, the captain came down to check himself. I told him perhaps some children were playing with it but there didn't seem to be any round, or it could be a fault with the mechanism or even his panel. He agreed and we decided to monitor and see what happened next.

So, I kept a close eye on the door. Sure enough, an hour or so later a little, old lady went to the toilet opposite Door Three Left. She came out and promptly pulled the door lock lever! I couldn't believe what I had just seen! I ran over to her and asked her why she had done that.

"Well, darlin', I am pulling the flush of course."

I explained to her that the flush was *inside* the toilet and pointed it to her. She laughed and said, "How can anyone see that small handle waaaay down there?"

She could barely see it as she was visually impaired with thick glasses. And to be honest with you, those flush handles *are* very small, so I guess she came out and saw a nice big lever with a knob, she could grab hold of and see properly.

I started chatting to her and she told me she had just been to see her grandchildren in the UK and was now returning to Kingston, how it had warmed her heart to see them and to have all the attention showered on her. Jamaicans, like the Indians, have huge respect for their elders and it was lovely to see the pride this lady had in her family.

No sooner had I finished chatting to her, when I was called to the back galley. They needed all hands, on deck as there seemed to be a bit of a riot brewing. It had all started because of some *supposedly* racial comment by either a Jamaican or a non-Jamaican. No one knew but now there was a group of young Jamaican men, promising to punch the 'living daylights' out of some other young British men, on the opposite side of the aisle. They were all pretty drunk.

On seeing how tall, big and strapping the Jamaicans were, the British lads found some humility from somewhere and tried to calm the Jamaicans down. But the Jamaicans were having none of it and were now riled-up. The crew had informed the captain and he had unlocked the restraint kit and had it at the ready, in case it was needed. The crew decided it was now time to at least take it down to the galley and keep it there, in case we needed to use it. So while a few of them went to the flight deck to discreetly bring it down, some of us went to try to placate the Jamaicans once again.

I have to say, even I was a little bit concerned as to what might happen on board that day. However, as we were trying to talk to the young men, I suddenly had a brainwave. I indicated to my colleagues to meet me back in the galley. By this time, the others had already brought the restraint kit down and I said, "Can you let me try something first? I think it might work."

They were reluctant as the situation was getting quite rowdy and other passengers were beginning to get up from their seats and come into the galley out of the line of fire.

"What are you going to do, Charlotte?" one of my colleagues said sarcastically, "flutter your eye lids at them?"

"Oh, that's not a bad idea," I replied, equally sarcastically, with an extra pinch of mockery. Then I turned serious.

"But no, perhaps something a bit more effective than that," I said and went over to the little old lady who was sitting at the front of the same cabin. I explained the situation very quickly and she said, "Don't worry, darlin'. You just lead me to dem."

I took her to them and indicated who I thought was the instigator in the group. She went right up to him and waved her finger at him in textbook fashion and said in her broad Jamaican accent, "Now, what is all this raucous about?"

"No, ma'am," I interjected, "that's the crew you're talking to." She was as blind as a bat. I turned her around to the right person and she squinted her eyes to look at him. "Oh dear, look at you," she said, clearing her glasses. "You are as black as they come, boy! How could I have mistaken that man for you?" She pointed to a completely different crew member than the one she had spoken to. "Now, you listen here. Why are you frightening these nice people?"

The young man's demeanour changed straight away. He softened his tone and said, "You don't understand, Mother, they started it and we have to defend ourselves. You see, it's a matter of pride."

"Oh, sonny, you don't know the first thing about pride. You haven't lived long enough, my child."

This annoyed him and he raised his voice to her and said, "Mother, please, leave this to us to deal with. Now step out of the way."

With that she raised her hand as high as it would go (which was not very high as she was a tiny, little thing) and brought it down in a swift motion, making direct contact with his cheek, resulting in a resounding *slap*! There was a unanimous, synchronised gasp from both crew and passengers, including the young Jamaicans and British.

The old lady stood there stoic, unafraid and defiant, staring him straight in the eyes. The young ring leader rubbed his cheek.

She continued as if nothing had happened. "I have grandchildren older than you and I am not afraid to raise my hand to them. Your mother would be ashamed of you! Now sit down and let these nice people enjoy the rest of their flight."

There was no need for the restraint kit that day. Mrs. Jones was thanked by both the flight and cabin crew, cheered by the passengers and the crew praised my ingenuity. I was a hero for at least an hour after that but Mrs Jones was a hero for a lifetime and I added her to my ever-growing 'list of bravest people'.

Life on a Postcard No. 44
How Do You Get Blood Off A Wooden Floor?

Soon after we met, Gayem came to live with me for a few months due to his 'house being completely renovated, darling. I just cannot abide carpets that are more than six months old'. He vacuumed them every day, so no wonder they were worn out in six months. He couldn't vacuum my house as it had wooden floors but that didn't stop him from giving them a high-gloss polish, each day he was in the country.

One such day after a high gloss, I walked into the lounge after a flight, slipped on the wooden floor that had been polished within an inch of its life, went arse over tits and fell hard, cracking my head open.

I shouted for Gayem who, you would have thought would certainly have made a drama out of this but he just stood over me and said, "Well, what do you want me to do?" I explained to him that there might be a minor problem with my head and then when he saw the blood seeping out from under me, the drama finally kicked in.

Shriek, shriek! "You're..." *shriek*, "bleeding!" *Scream, screech, screech*! Flap hands, flap hands, fan face with hands, *shriek*! "You're bleeding all over the floor I've just polished!"

Not quite what I was hoping for, but it had the desired effect, in that he called the ambulance if only to stop me bleeding and get me off his lovely, polished wooden floor.

The paramedics asked him to accompany us, which he did reluctantly but was most put out that they did not let him clean the floor first. During the ambulance ride I heard two things: my erratic breathing through the oxygen mask and Gayem asking the paramedic repeatedly, "How do you get blood out of wooden floors? You must see blood on carpets and floors all the time in your line of work. You must have *some* idea about getting the blood out."

When we got to the hospital, the trauma nurse asked Gayem to wait with me. He asked me, "Do you really want me to wait here?" to which I nodded, as I was not able to talk. He was very upset and said, "Well, I wish they'd hurry up. It's nearly 10.30 and *Richard and Judy* will be starting soon."

He was also most put out that he had to come and get me the next day. My head had been stitched up and I was still coming out of the anaesthetic when he turned up. All I could hear the nurse saying to me was, "Hubby's here, Hubby's here!" in a very shrill voice. "Wake up, Charlotte, Hubby's here!"

I couldn't decide who was more delirious, me or her. Surely even a visually impaired person could see he was delightedly, openly gay. Even blurry eyed, I could see him mincing his way to my bed.

On exiting the hospital, I noticed a car waiting for us. It was Freya. We got in.

"Biggest drama queen in the world called me this morning and insisted I come and help him as he couldn't cope with you. I was right in the middle of a very interesting sex experiment with Adrian, but oh no, I had to leave that behind and come and *save* him."

"Purleeese," Gayem said. "Do we really need to be that graphic?"

They started to argue. "Seriously? You talk about graphic?

What about the time Charlotte was interested in cottaging and we all sat in the car in the dark watching, while you gave us some gory stories about that? Did I even flinch? What about the time you described feltching and rimming to us in great detail? Did I wince even for a second? What about the time you told us you went to an S&M bar in America somewhere? You told us as soon as you walked in, a chap pulled your trousers down and you started to introduce yourself and he said — 'woah, dude, too much information, maaan'. So, don't talk to me about *graphic*."

We got home and I tried to rest but all I could hear was the two of them arguing, about how Freya needed to be the one looking after me as she was the best to do it and Gayen saying she was welcome to it, if she thought she could do a better job at keeping a clean and tidy environment for me to get well in.

"The whole bloody reason she was in hospital," Freya continued, "is because *you* kept the house too bloody clean."

I had to get up from my sick bed and ask them to keep it down as I was trying to rest.

"Go back to bed and rest, Charlotte," Freya said. "I will sort this out."

"It's you trying to sort that out which is stopping me from resting," I mumbled but didn't see any point in even trying to get them to stop.

Life on a Postcard No. 45
What's an Engine on Fire Between Friends?

I think I was getting the same sort of reputation as a black cat or an evil talisman. Crew now started to panic when they saw my name on a roster. I either seemed to have a medical emergency or a technical one. No sooner had I recovered from my head injury, when I was off to Newark. Although Freya and I tried to fly together, it didn't always work out that way. However, this time Freya had engineered this trip with me. She had been on a New York flight but swapped to be on my Newark one, insisting I needed support.

The only support I would need was propping up the bar when we got there.

We had just taken off and were still strapped into our seats when we heard a loud bang on the left-hand side of the aircraft. My jump seat happened to be in the middle of the aircraft on the left-hand side, with a clear view of the engines. As I looked across to see what that noise was. I could see flames coming out of the Number Two engine. We were on a 747 so thankfully we still had three engines left, however, the flames were quite vicious. I pretended not to notice and smiled sweetly at the passengers opposite.

They looked at me, then looked back at the engine, then looked at me again as if to say, 'Surely you can't expect us to not notice?' One of them started to point to the engine. I smiled sweetly again.

"Nothing to worry about at all. Just the friction," I

reassured them.

The next thing I heard was the emergency call from the flight deck. This was in code so that passengers didn't panic when they heard it! The passengers kept trying to tell me about the flames, almost doubting their own vision as I was trying to be calm about it. Freya called me from the back of the aircraft. "You know the number two engine is on fire?"

"Yes." I smiled as I spoke, so as not to alarm the passengers

"Do you think we will have to evacuate?" There was a decided air of excitement in her voice. Not fear, not alarm, no concern, not even a thought for the passengers.

"I don't know," I said, again between clenched, smiling teeth

"Ooooh, we might crash," she said, enthusiastically.

"I certainly hope not," I said. "Why don't I talk to you later when we have a bit more time." I put the phone down and by now the passengers who were still really quite calm, considering they could see fire in an engine, had told some other passengers, who were also really calm but concerned and they now addressed this with me.

"Excuse me, you do know that the engine is on fire, don't you?"

"Oh, that's perfectly natural," I said and no sooner had I finished my sentence, when the Captain came on the PA system.

"Ladies and gentlemen, some of you might have noticed that we have a slight *technical* problem with one of our engines. (Understatement of the year!) While we could continue quite safely onto Newark with three engines, (Yeah but not with one of them continuing to burn), there is the slight (definite) possibility of a fire and so we are going to return (fly like the wind) to London and change aircraft. I will give you further instructions once we are close to landing. (You might not be exiting the flight the way you got on!) You will now notice us circling as we lighten the aircraft by getting rid of some of our fuel, so that the aircraft isn't too heavy when we land. (So we don't all crash and burn.)"

As I looked across at the engine, the flames were getting bigger and angrier than before. I could see the fire extinguishers in the engine trying to fight the flames but they were losing the battle.

We were then allowed to stand up and go through the cabins checking seat belts and reassuring passengers. Then the Captain came on again.

"Ladies and gentlemen, we will shortly be landing in London. Please leave the aircraft in an orderly manner. (Don't kill each other trying to get out.) There is nothing to worry about. (But we are shitting our pants up here!) Please follow the instructions from the cabin crew. You might notice some fire engines and trucks as we land that will accompany the aircraft to a remote part of the runway. Please do not let this alarm you. (They are only trying to save us from turning into toast.) You might also see some white foam being poured onto the engine and this is merely to extinguish the fire."

Two minutes later he was back on the PA.

'Er… ladies and gentlemen. Cancel that. We will be evacuating the aircraft. Repeat: there will be a full evacuation. Cabin crew, please prepare to evacuate on landing." (Shit has now truly and completely hit the fan!) I looked down the aisle at Freya, who was punching the air excitedly with her fist and mouthing the word 'yes' over and over again. Luckily, this was out of the view of passengers.

In spite of this announcement, I was amazed at how calm the passengers were and listened to our instructions.

We landed with a *thud*, could see the emergency trucks waiting for us and following us as quickly as they could along the runway. The brakes were applied with full force as we started to shudder down the taxiway. However, the flames must have caught a burst of air or fuel, or a combination of both and now even I couldn't keep my composure as the right-hand side of the aircraft also caught fire. I got the passengers to keep their heads down and finally, after what seemed like a whole year, the aircraft came to a stop.

The evacuation was initiated and we started to evacuate only from the left side. Even though those trucks were on us as speedily as a gull swoops on its prey and even though they engulfed us with their foam as quickly as they could, they still couldn't put out the fire soon enough and now practically, the whole aircraft was burning.

By now we had evacuated most of the passengers but some were still in shock and wouldn't move and some had been injured on landing and couldn't move. The situation was desperate as there was thick, black smoke billowing through the whole cabin and we had to crawl on our hands and knees just to be able to breathe. The captain ordered us to leave the aircraft as now we couldn't even see our hands in front of our faces. We were all choking, one of the crew had already passed out with the fumes and we'd had no time to put on our oxygen masks.

The crew started to jump down the slides. Freya was now at my door and I shouted to her that there were still passengers in the cabin. She said, "Okay, let's go get them."

"But you do realise we could be burnt alive as well?" I said.

"We can't just leave them there," she said.

"No, you're right, but we might die trying. You okay with that?" I said, coughing and spluttering.

"Don't be silly. We aren't going to die." (Cough, cough, splutter, splutter.)

One passenger was unconscious in their seat and it took both Freya and I to get her out of her seat and onto the floor. We were now ready to pass out ourselves. I'm not sure how but we managed to drag her to the door and fling her down the slide. Just as we did so I felt a hand grab me. It was one of the firemen. He was on an airlift, trying to get me to either go down the slide or get onto the airlift with him.

Thinking about it now, both Freya and I were so filled with smoke by that time that we were delirious.

I pushed him off me and shouted that there were more passengers inside. He said we couldn't help that, he needed to get us out first and then he would go in for the others.

Somehow, we didn't believe him but he persisted and got hold of my other arm. I kept trying to drag myself back into the cabin and he kept trying to drag me out. I shouted to Freya to hit him with something to get him off me. She grabbed the nearest fire extinguisher and hit him on the head. This stunned him for a bit and he released his grip.

So, when the media said that not a single aircraft fire extinguisher was used on board that day, they were wrong. We certainly put one to good use.

Freya and I ran back in and managed to get the last three passengers out before collapsing on top of the slide. By this time, the very annoyed fireman had now regained his composure and pushed us down the slide, where his colleagues caught us. But we were already unconscious.

Did the next day's papers have pictures of the burning plane, the plane landing on the runway, the passengers who went through the trauma of an evacuation, the Captain who had controlled and landed the aircraft so well?

No! The only pictures splashed all over the national papers were pictures of me pushing the poor fireman and Freya hitting him repeatedly with a fire extinguisher.

The headlines read:

'FIGHTING FIRE WITH FIREMAN'

'NOW THAT'S WHAT WE CALL PUTTING OUT A FIRE(MAN!)'

'IS THAT HOW YOU USE A FIRE EXTINGUISHER?'

You get the point. Of course, we were praised for saving the last few passengers but were put through a gruelling enquiry, debrief, post-brief and any other brief you could possibly think of. Luckily, the fireman didn't sue us or claim injuries. We heard the expression 'diminished responsibility due to inhalation of smoke' more times than we cared to count.

Most crew were now scared to fly with us and we were forced to take some time off and given counselling, whether we liked it or not. I took the time off to take my parents away — yes, you guessed it — on a flight! You know what they say — if you fall off a horse...

Life on a Postcard No. 46
The Bird

Initially, Mother was delighted with Father's retirement and had dreams of travelling all over the world with him — and me! But slowly, it started to dawn on her that retirement with Father was not all it was cracked up to be. Father was a workaholic and therefore, without work, he was suffering greatly. He was restless, irritable and constantly needed to be kept busy. Mother got to a point where she was now breaking appliances just so that he could fix them and in doing so kept him out of her hair.

He was there when she woke up, when she was cooking, when she was playing Canasta with her regular foursome each week — he was there *all the time*!

She confessed to me that she was finding this difficult and that he was probably finding it difficult not working.

"Well, why don't you just send him back to work then?" I asked.

"It's not that easy, Lottie. He's retired and they've already given him his carriage clock, as it were."

"So why can't he go off and be a consultant or something?" I said. "Someone, somewhere must want the expertise that he has in his brain."

Mother's eyes lit up. "Yes! An ex-colleague of his asked him to come and work with him once he retired, as he was in need of someone with Dad's expertise on foreign affairs. But how do I broach the subject? He seems to be really enjoying his retirement."

So as I had some forced time off, I said I would take them on a trip and we would tackle this together.

The trip I took them on was a once-in-a-lifetime one. As I worked for the airlines, I not only got concessions on my own airline but on others as well, so decided to take them to New York, on Concorde!

We were all very excited and even Father hadn't been on Concorde in all his travels with the 'Government'. We arrived at the Concorde lounge and waited for our flight, stuffing our faces with caviar, smoked salmon and Champagne. Then I realised that our boarding cards didn't have a gate number on them. Knowing you always had to have a gate number, this concerned me somewhat. I went to the Concorde reception desk in the lounge and was confronted by the snootiest person I had ever met in my life. Her nose was on an imaginary string which seemed to be getting pulled closer and closer to the ceiling, as I approached her. She wasn't aware I was staff so gave me her saccharine smile as I neared the desk.

"Excuse me," I said, "but I don't seem to see a gate number on my boarding card. Where do we go, to get on the Concorde?" Now, of course, I had given the game away and she knew this was my first time on Concorde. The imaginary string must have been given a sudden jerk again as this time, her nose was virtually vertical. She took a deep breath, as her nose was now pointing directly at the ceiling and said, "Madam does not have to go to Concorde. Concorde will come to Madam."

And with all the flourish of a 1970s TV hostess showing off the prizes you could win on a game show, she made a hand-sweeping gesture towards a door. It started to open at that moment and revealed a glass walkway, at the end of which was

Concorde! She was right — it literally came to us.

Why glass walkway you might ask? So that passengers can see the majesty of Concorde as they walk towards it but more importantly, others can you boarding Concorde which is equally if not more important!

It was the narrowest aircraft I had been on. The seats were tiny, bucket, leather seats, and the cockpit was probably built by the Oompa Loompas.

Mother and I sat on one side of the aisle together and Father sat by himself on the other side of the narrow aisle. Mother and I were so excited we were nearly jumping up and down in our seats as we were about to take off. We looked across at Father as if to say, 'Isn't this amazing?' when I noticed — as we were taking off in one of the most iconic passenger aircraft of our times; taking off in an aeroplane that most people could only dream of travelling on — there was Father reading *The Sun* newspaper and not only that... he had paused to look at page three!

"*Dad*!" I said in a loud stage whisper. "What are you doing! Here we are taking off in the fastest passenger jet in the world and you're reading *The Sun*! Do you realise we'll be arriving in New York before we've even taken off from London but you have the cheek to read *The Sun* as we are taking off! At least show a bit of respect and read *The Times*."

"Well, darling, I don't see what I am supposed to do while we're taking off. It's no different from another aircraft."

I gave up!

At least I got to see New York this time, as I'd been too exhausted the last time. We were able to experience New York together. I insisted we went to the top of the Empire State Building and with unsuspecting parents in tow, I intended to get to the highest point and scream from there — which I did.

I stuck my head through the bars and just screamed and screamed. It was quite therapeutic and completely released any stress I felt.

Another tick for Zaheer, as he had talked about that often: 'I want to go right to the top of the Empire State Building and just scream'.

Mother was still fussing about it all the way down and all the way back to the hotel: how embarrassing it had been, how everyone had stared at her and she'd had to pretend that I had a strange and very little-known condition called "heightitis" where great heights made me scream. I was actually quite impressed with Mother for thinking about that one on the spot.

However, there was still the 'Father issue' to tackle, so Mother and I hatched a plan. We decided to go for dinner on our last night, to the revolving restaurant at the Marriot on Broadway. The restaurant revolved slowly so we could see a panoramic view of the whole city. The only problem was, that each time we tried to go back to the buffet it had moved!

Mother said she was getting very confused — it didn't take much to confuse her — Father told her to enjoy the ride.

It was then that we started to talk about Father's work. I asked him if he missed it and he said he did. I asked him why he had retired, to which he said he wanted to enjoy his retirement while he was still young enough to enjoy it. And besides, Mother told him to retire. She then interjected and vehemently denied that fact.

She and Father then engaged in an extremely boring argument covering dates, times and circumstances wherein these conversations had taken place. I finally put a stop to it by asking Mother, "Where's the buffet now, Mum?" That distracted her completely.

I asked Father whether he had thought of using all his

knowledge and experience and perhaps doing some consultancy work.

"Well, an ex-colleague has started a good, little business of his own and asked me to join him but I refused, as your mother wouldn't have liked it'.

Mum, who was still straining her neck to see where the buffet had moved to, said over her shoulder, "Darling, I would have been very happy for you to join him."

"Well, why didn't you say so in the first place, woman? I'll call him as soon as I get back! I've been so bored at home and I'm sure I've been under your feet, darling."

Mum: "Of course you haven't, darling. I've really enjoyed having you but I'm thinking about your happiness now and if that makes you happy, then that's what you should do."

Dad: "That's great, darling and it's not like I won't be around at all. It won't be like I've gone back to work full-time. I will still be able to spend time with you."

Mum: "Oh, don't you worry about that, my darling. If it means it takes you away from me then that's the way it will have to be and if it means travelling as well, then I will just have to deal with that but the most important thing, is that you are doing what you want to do."

Well, now I knew what marriage was all about: lying through your teeth with a straight face.

It had now been three years since Zaheer had died and I was slowly beginning to feel human again. I decided the time had come to at least write to the Modis. They had now resorted to emails, as letters and calls had not worked with me. I sat down and got as far as pressing 'reply', then I shut the computer down again.

My dreams of Marvin seemed to have died down recently but then I had another one. This time he went to the post office and got into some strange situation, where he ended up with stamps all over him. I thought of going to visit a doctor but what would I tell them? That I was having some very animated dreams about a toy moose that came to life?

Life on a Postcard No. 47
Flying High

Dear Mother,

Rio was my most recent trip, where it's the done thing, to go hang-gliding, so two of the flight crew and I decided we were going to brave it. We went up this windy, scary road to the top of the Cocovado Mountain, on a peak close to the statue of Jesus Christ. Our guide informed us we would jump off this peak and land on the beach. When I stood on the edge to look down, I decided *nothing* was going to make me just jump off that cliff with just a pair of cloth wings on a steel stand. The flight crew finally convinced me that if they were going to die, I was going to have to die with them. We did a few dry runs before I was paired with a very large, black, South-American man who said, "There are a few rules: you have to start running and when you get to the edge, you just keep running. Don't look down and *do not* stop when you get to the edge. And finally, grab hold of this and hold it tight." Till today, Mother, I don't know what I was asked to grab hold of but I do know I held it very tight and didn't let go till we landed.

We started running and to give me my due, I managed to jump off a cliff as high as the Empire State Building right into just only thin air. When I finally opened my eyes, there was a bird flying next to us. It was the closest thing I will ever get to actually flying. We soared past buildings below us and my big, black man said, "You're quite light, so I think I can take you up to the statue."

We did a few rounds, as we climbed higher and higher up the mountain and the higher we flew, the closer he managed to get us to the statue and the tighter the circles became. We were then face to face with the face of Jesus — one of the most awe-inspiring, fascinating and yes, I would even go so far as to say, *religious* experiences of my life.

We finally landed on the beach. Zaheer would have loved it.

Life on a Postcard No. 48
Nah, That's Not A Knife, This Is A Knife

If I ever doubted Freya's coolness, I never did again after this night. After Rio, we had met for our usual dinner but this time decided to go to a night club. Freya had heard about this club, when she was having her latest tattoo done. She had one on her wrist which said, 'Keep Calm; Smoke Weed', and another one on her shoulder of Darth Vader. She was a huge fan of *Star Wars* because she believed that we all lived with our own fantasies and the one she wanted to live in, was *Star Wars*, where good versus evil was clearly demarcated and everyone knew their place. Her latest tattoo was, 'Good Point, well made', which she had tattooed just above her pelvis, on the right-hand side at an angle.

Me: "Why in god's name?"

Freya: "It's something Adrian says all the time to annoy me."

Me: "Oh la la! You *do* love him!"

Freya: "Don't be silly."

Me: "Yes, you do! Yes, you do!"

Freya: "*Love* is too strong a word."

Me: "Yes, of course it is, luvvie! You have your boyfriend's favourite expression tattooed on your pelvis but clearly 'love' isn't the word for it. Please tell me you've actually told him you love him."

Freya: "Of course not. Why do I need to tell him?"

Me: "Has he told you?"

Freya: "Every day since I met him."

Me: "And you haven't said it back?"

Freya: "No. Why do I need to?"

Me: "Do you love him?"

Freya: "Love is just a concept. It's not an emotion. You can have all kinds of different types of love. You have a mother's love, love for a particular type of food. There's a huge misconception out there that love is a feeling or emotion. Feelings and emotions last, love changes all the time. It's…"

Me: "Stop bullshitting and giving me your hard-hitting philosophy, right now. You *have* to tell him. Doesn't he ask you?"

Freya: "Every day since I met him."

Me: "You need to tell him."

Freya: "He knows."

Me: "It doesn't matter. He still needs to hear it."

Freya: "Why does he? I don't need to hear it and I don't need to say it."

Me: "Tell him now!"

Freya: "Oh, all right, if it's going to make you happy."

She dialled his number, he picked up. She said, "Charlotte thinks I need to tell you I love you. So, I love you. Now don't expect me to say it every day or in fact ever again."

I heard him say, "You don't know how much that means to me."

"Okay, good. Off to a nightclub now. Catch you later."

And that is all you could expect to get from her; take it or leave it — that amazing moment of the first time she told him she loved him, over a phone, done in two minutes.

We tried to find the nightclub a fellow tattoo fan had told her about and walked up and down some of the dodgiest streets off Leicester Square. Finally, don't ask me how, we managed to find the back door of the night club and tried to open it. As we did so, I saw an arm grab Freya by the neck and drag her backwards. The arm's hand had a knife attached to it and was right on Freya's jugular. At first, I thought this was Freya having a laugh but soon realised it was for real.

"Let's have it," he said. I stood there transfixed, calm but scared. I looked over at Freya but she looked more annoyed than scared.

"What are you waiting for?" the mugger said. "This isn't a movie. I'm not going to say, "Your money or your life," or "Hand over the cash and no one gets hurt." Just give me your purses, now!" I threw mine at him and he caught it with his other hand. Freya started to bend down slowly.

"What are you doing, bitch?" he asked, nastily.

Freya paused for a second and said slowly, as if she was talking to a moron or a small child trying to explain something in detail that they don't understand, "I'm trying to get my money. I'm about to step into a night club, so you can see I haven't got a purse on me. I always keep my money in my shoe."

"Okay, slowly and carefully. This isn't a prop knife I have here; this will draw blood." And just in case Freya doubted him, he pushed the knife closer to her throat.

Freya removed her stiletto and holding onto the heel, though she was unable to see what she was doing, as casually as she would lift a glass of wine from a table, she lifted the shoe over her shoulder and rammed the heel backwards into his face, managing to do some serious damage to his left eye.

He let out an eye-popping scream which attracted a couple of drunk teenagers, who started to make their way into the alley. He ran past them as fast as he could, dropping the shoe next to them.

Freya walked over to them while they were still staring open-mouthed, casually picked up her shoe and very

'Bondesque' said, "Now that's what I call an eyeful."

I dined out on that story for months, Gayen dined out on it for a whole year and Adrian wouldn't let her go anywhere without him after that. Can you imagine how much that pleased her?

Life on a Postcard No. 49
Reassess, Revisit and Repeat

It had been two years now since I started flying. Mother was calmer about it, as she continued to receive her regular postcards and Father was fascinated with my stories both on and off the aircraft. I was fairly jet-lagged after Rio but went over to see them and stayed the night, as they had been quite insistent. During dinner they were fairly quiet. I could see them sideways glancing at each other; a common practice as you know by now, any time they wanted to bring something up. I felt myself twitching, starting from the tips of my toes, then my legs started moving up and down. Finally, I couldn't stand it any longer and before I made like a Tasmanian Devil and started spinning around the room, I threw my hands up in the air and shouted, "Whaaattt?"

As usual, Mother moved her chin upwards as if to say to Father, 'You say it'. He did the same to her but I could only stand the chin push-ups a couple more times before I screamed, "Just spit it out!"

"Well, darling, the thing is, darling," Mother started to say. "How is your travelling going by the way?"

"Mum, get on with it," I said, irritably.

Father interjected this time, "Lottie, Charlo... tte. We've had several calls from the Modis and they really do want to talk to you, darling. I know it's difficult for you but really, it's the best thing for you to do."

"For goodness sake, Dad! It's been three years now and I

really want to move on. Is it the best thing for me or for them?" I asked, indignantly. Now I was on the defensive.

"Well, darling," Mother said, "they've been through the worst and most tragic loss you can ever imagine and you were the closest person to him after his family. They really would just like to talk."

I looked at my parents and knew they must have had some sad conversations with them but I was past that now. I had moved on and I needed to make a clean break.

"Please tell them from me that I love them very much, I think of them very often but I need to move on with my life. By going back, even with a phone call, would undo all the effort I have put into moving on. I'm sure they will understand."

I left my parents with that sick feeling in the pit of my stomach, I knew ever so well. I felt it often and had learnt to live with it. It had been over three years now since Zaheer had died. Why were people trying to take me back there and pull me down and make me relive that? I had moved on and so they should let me.

Life on a Postcard No. 50
Singapore

Dear Mother,

Singapore has had many beginnings but the uppermost in local memory was January 1891, which saw the founding of modern Singapore by Stamford Raffles, an Englishman, who claimed the island as a trading settlement for the East India Company.

The rest, as they say, is history.

Singapore is a mixed bowl of fried rice as far as religions and cultures are concerned: Buddhism, Taoism, Islam, Christianity and Hinduism are Singapore's major religions. They all consider themselves Singaporean and would never live anywhere else.

Singaporeans are very proud of their country and do have much to be proud of. They say that they have learnt from other countries and have taken the best from them; that their country is clean, green, has very little poverty, very little crime and the people are content and happy.

That might be so but I had a slightly different view.

While there is a lot about Singapore that I love, I found it too clinical, too artificial, everything was man-made — it had no character. When I came through Customs, they confiscated my chewing gum!

Singaporeans were very proud of their law enforcement. Sometimes criticised for being too harsh and brutal, the local people believed it worked.

As we landed in Singapore, we were obliged to deliver this warning over the PA: 'Ladies and gentlemen, the death penalty is mandatory for anyone convicted of trafficking or transporting drugs.' Who could forget the American teenager who'd been flogged for vandalism?

The way I look at it, Mother, yes it might be very harsh but… he'll never do that again now, will he? (I wonder whether I should bring Cousin Alicia's boy with me here next time…)

Their no-nonsense attitude to crime paid.

As the crime rate increased around the world, in Singapore it decreased. There were not many places in the world where I could take a walk at 2 a.m. and feel safe. Due to jet lag, I was walking the streets each night. On one of those walks I came across a very interesting statue by Salvador Dalì; a sort of a modern-art skeleton. The head was hollow with a brain dangling in it and the body was hollow with a heart dangling in it and under the sculpture it had an inscription by Dalì himself: 'When you come to visit Singapore, do so with an open heart and open mind — like I did'. I thought that was very clever and changed my opinion about modern art but only to a certain extent and it also encouraged me to look into Dalì's work a bit more.

No postcard about Singapore would be complete without the 'S' word! Here you can literally *shop* till you and your bank balance both drop. Unfortunately, Singapore was not the cheap shoppers' paradise it used to be. The standard of living was very high. For tourists, the prices were prohibitive and even residents accepted that it was an expensive place. One of the residents told me, 'We go to London to shop. That's how expensive it is here!'

Unlike many other countries in the Far East and India, bargaining was generally not acceptable in Singapore.

While I was in Singapore itself, I had another weird dream about Marvin. This time it was about Marvin being on an aeroplane. I put it down to the fact that I had just been on such a long sector and was jet-lagged.

Life on a Postcard No. 51
Keeping Us Abreast of Things

On returning from Singapore, I had a phone call from Freya. "Adrian proposed. I'm going to say no."

That was so typical of Freya: no mincing her words, no preamble, no nonsense. "Okay," I said, "and give me just one good reason why."

"I will when we meet." The phone went dead.

Freya had changed our dinner date to a day later, as Adrian couldn't make that day and she wanted me to be there when she told him. I knew from past experience, that no amount of telling Freya how inappropriate this was and how much it would hurt Adrian, would make her see sense.

This was another one of Freya's, "I really don't want a drama, so I need to have someone else there when I tell him."

Freya was waiting for me when I arrived and Adrian followed shortly afterwards. He wasn't expecting her to give him his answer in front of me, so I was the only one feeling awkward.

Freya spoke. "I have breast cancer. They have to remove the right one, then they'll do a biopsy and let me know if I'm going to live or die."

She then turned to Adrian and said, "I can't marry you. Now I need to eat. I'm starving."

She started to call the waiter and order from the menu.

I could see by Adrian's expression that he was still trying to assimilate the information he had just been given: firstly, to assess whether it was true, and secondly, to identify whether he had actually heard right.

I had had enough. This time I was not going to let her get away with, 'That's just Freya, that's the way she is.'

"Just a minute," I said. This was directed at Freya. I then turned to the waiter and said, "Could you give us a couple of minutes, please?"

Me: "Oh no Madame, not this time you don't."

Freya: "What do you mean?"

Me: "This time we are going to play by my rules."

Freya: "What are you on about, woman?"

Me: "When and how did you find out?"

Freya: "Last week, felt a lump, had some pain."

Me: "What exactly have they told you about it?"

Freya: "The right breast has had it; needs to go."

Me: "So what they are saying? Has the cancer spread throughout the right breast and it needs to be removed but there's no cancer in the left?"

Freya: "Yes there is but not as bad. They will do a biopsy and let me know. We have just repeated a conversation that I put in one sentence at the beginning. Tell me, do you know anything more than what I told you a few minutes ago? No. So there you have it. Breast cancer, right has to go, will do biopsy and let me know."

Me: "I can't believe it."

Freya: "Yeah and I don't even smoke. Go figure."

Adrian and I looked at each other in genuine shock. This time it was Adrian who spoke.

Adrian: "You *don't* smoke?"

Freya: "Well, not cigs at least."

185

Adrian: "No, but you have a healthy side order of weed with your main course on a regular basis."

Freya: "There is no connection between weed and cancer."

Adrian: "There is now. How do you know what kind of substances and artificial stuff they put in there?"

Before she could answer, we saw someone familiar walking towards us. It was Gayem.

Me: "Are you crazy? You can't tell him."

Freya: "He has to know."

Me: "Yes but behind closed doors, in a soft, padded soundproof cell, where he can bounce off the walls and shriek all he likes. Not in a public place, where there is an abundance of human life."

Freya: "Oh, DK'll be fine."

Freya couldn't bring herself to call him Gayem, so 'Drama Kween' was her name for him.

I was half-inclined to believe she was right, when I remembered my fall and how he couldn't be bothered until he saw blood on his shiny floor.

He sashayed around the table, kissing us in turn. "How nice of Frey to include me in your weekly dinner."

"Only tonight," Freya said, but Gayem didn't hear her. He continued, "You won't believe the week I've had. Firstly, Truly Scrumptious — his poodle — had to have her shots and then... Oh, can I have a G&T please, with a twist?" he said to the waiter and continued seamlessly without a break. "And you know how she gets when she has to have her shots..."

Freya waited for the right moment when he was in full flow, G&T safely in his custody. He had just taken a swig of it when she then took great pleasure in interjecting with, "I have breast cancer. Right, one has to go."

It reminded me of the time Father had broken the news to Mother about Hyderabad. Freya was in the direct line of fire but was clever enough to duck, as she said those words and therefore it was Adrian who got an eyeful of liquid that shot straight out of Gayem's mouth.

"Who's cancer? Who's right and who's one?" A jumbled Gaymen stumbled over his words.

None of us spoke. We just gave it some time to sink in.

He apologised to Adrian while trying to wipe his face and trying to clarify what he had heard all at the same time.

Freya explained it to him with as much brevity as she had explained it to us.

I guess you could have expected the next question from Gayem, as sure as you could expect Miss Marple to solve her mysteries.

"Are you going to die?" Gayem asked.

"Maybe," replied Freya.

Gayem started to breathe deeply and then the very sharp intakes of breath began. "I... I... can't breathe, I can't breathe."

I could feel the hysteria building and before it could reach a crescendo, I reached for his G&T, turned to Freya and said, "Did I not warn you about this?" as I threw what was left of the drink, sharply into his face.

Gayem spluttered and gasped for a bit and then when he finally managed to catch his breath, he shrieked, "What did you do that for?"

"To calm you down," I said, "but clearly it hasn't worked."

Shortly afterwards, Freya went in for her op. We were all

by her side when she went in and we were all by her side when she came out. We waited with bated breath for her to finally open her eyes. She looked at each of our anxious faces in turn and the first words she said were, "You know, I have always wanted a big bust? (She was a 30A.) Well, they have promised me I can have Double Ds!" She sounded as excited as she could, still under the effect of the anaesthesia.

Then we had to play the waiting game. In the meantime, life had to carry on.

Life on a Postcard No. 52
Chicken and First Aid

Dear Mother,

My Dallas flight started out as a flight like any other. The drinks and meals had been served and we were two hours into our flight. The passengers had settled down to watch the movie. As I looked down the aisle to make sure all was well, a man beckoned to me and pointed to a large, Texan gentleman sitting beside him. The Texan had a red face and tears streaming down his cheeks. Either he had been reading the inflight magazine or he was choking.

Deciding against the former, I led him firmly and quickly to the toilet. Bending him over the seat I started to hit him as hard as I could between his shoulder blades. Everything I had learnt in training kept flashing through my mind: *Place the passenger over the seat and hit firmly between the shoulder blades four times*. But this was reality. I had learnt pretty soon that reality was very different from the calm clinical atmosphere of the training room.

Although I wasn't hysterical, I wasn't exactly calm either. I wasn't hitting him sharply between the shoulder blades, I was whacking him as hard as I could while shaking him at the same time, trying anything I could to get the obstruction out. If I could have turned him upside down, I would have done. I could see his face in the mirror of the toilet cubicle. It had now changed to a pale shade of green.

One of my colleagues came out of the galley, saw me pounding this passenger and almost said, "Another one asked for a double gin and tonic, did he?" but she stopped short.

The 'hitting sharply between the shoulder blades' having had no effect at all, I decided to start the Heimlich manoeuvre, sometimes known as the abdominal thrust.

So with all my might, I started thrusting. I couldn't have cared less whether my hands were in the right position. I made a fist, placed it on his abdomen, grabbed my fist with my other hand and kept thrusting and shouting, "Cough, cough! Work with me! Work with me! You are *not* working with me!"

The poor man was gasping for air and I was criticising him for not being able to work with me.

He was now foaming at the mouth — another area they gloss over in training. They ask you to gently put your hand in the person's mouth and take away any debris and they describe it in such a way, that you almost look forward to doing it. Not in real life. I put my hand through all the foam and crap coming out of his mouth and took out anything in there. There was nothing.

Just when I thought I was running out of thrusts, he started spluttering. This was a new sign. He had foamed, he had gasped, he had sucked but he hadn't spluttered before.

Taking it as a good sign, I gave him one huge thrust and the piece of chicken which had nearly claimed his life, came shooting out of his mouth with no less speed than a shotgun. It swirled around and around the toilet bowl a couple of times like a coin in a charity swirl machine and then went down the hole out of sight. We both stared at it as it vanished from sight. Exhausted and emotional, we both sat down: he on the toilet seat and me on the crew seat just outside it. We didn't speak for at least five minutes. I gave him time to clean up and went to get him a glass of water. Then I took him to his seat, settled him in and didn't give him the option of 'chicken or beef' for the rest of the flight.

Life on a Postcard No. 53
Hair Today

Immediately after arriving back from Dallas, I went to see Freya who was soon to be discharged from hospital. They'd had to remove her right breast but managed to save her left one by removing the lump and had given her the first session of six obligatory chemo sessions, to ensure all the cells had been killed off. She would have to wait for her Double Ds till after her treatment was over.

When I walked into her room, she was sitting up in bed eating a boiled egg. Freya *loved* egg. We all wondered at one point, whether the excessive number of eggs had given her cancer. *Is that at all possible*? we thought. With the amount of eggs Freya ate, it certainly was possible.

With each chemo session, a bit more of her hair fell out. After the second session, before I visited Freya, I told her I had shaved off my hair in sympathy with her. When I got there, she took one look at me with my full head of hair and said, "Bitch! I thought you said you shaved off your hair."

I said, "I didn't say it was on my head now, did I?" Freya straightaway looked at my crotch and started laughing, picturing what that might look like!

Freya appreciated that, as it was the kind of thing she would have done. So each time she had chemo, I shaved my pubes.

Everyone thought it was funny except for Gayem, who couldn't appreciate the joke. "How can you joke like this when poor Frey has cancer?" But Freya was the one laughing the loudest.

However, her final session was particularly brutal and harsh as they 'wanted to catch each one of those slippery little suckers', a quote from Freya's least favourite movie *Pretty Woman*, as Freya did not do romance in any way, shape or form.

I had a brainwave. I asked Adrian to ask his barber if he would shave our hair and Adrian, Gaymen and I decided we were all going to do this en masse. We looked like some of the crew off *Star Trek*.

We all turned up completely bald to escort Freya out of hospital, after her final chemo session.

She looked exhausted and fed up and I had never seen that expression on her face: one of giving up. But then I had never seen the next expression either: one of surprise. Nothing ever surprised or moved Freya but today, she went through both of those emotions. That was enough for us and the fact that she looked at each and one of us in turn and said, "Hey thanks, guys. This really does mean a lot. And looking at you all standing in front of me, when you have made such a huge sacrifice, I can tell you something for sure — not one of you does bald as well as I do."

Life on a Postcard No. 54
One Eventful Night

I had now been flying for four years, in order to live Zaheer's life for him and to 'get away' from it all, though I wasn't quite sure what I was 'getting away' from, or for how long I needed to get away. However sometimes, as they say, fate plays a hand. This time, fate didn't just play a hand but grabbed me by the hair and swung me around — literally.

I was on a night flight back from Atlanta. Half of the crew were on their rest. The flight was largely full of businessmen and women, who were mostly sleeping after presumably busy schedules.

I was busy reading a gossip magazine when one of the male passengers came into the galley and he was hyperventilating. I started wondering about airline food again: could my parents really be right?

However, I could see he was having an anxiety attack. I quickly sat him down on the crew seat near the door and tried to grab for a sick bag for him to breathe into, while trying to get the attention of a colleague in the next galley. Just then, he shot up from the seat saying, "I gotta get outta here!" Although I sympathised with him completely, and couldn't have agreed more, I knew I had to do something to calm him down.

Before I could even say 'nutcase', he had grabbed hold of the door handle and was trying to open the door. At thirty-five thousand feet, that is never a good idea as most people know it can be injurious to your health, even more injurious to your health than smoking. However, what most people didn't know is that even if that handle were to be moved on a Boeing 747, the door wouldn't open due to the pressure outside being greater than inside. However, it was clearly not advisable to try mid-flight.

I grabbed him with all my strength. By then, another crew member was in the galley and I whispered to him to get the handcuffs to restrain the passenger. We were concerned about waking the other passengers and causing chaos and panic but at the same time, trying to be firm with him and whispering to him with a hisssssss, "Stop that right now. Let go or we will restrain you."

A passenger happened to come into the galley and saw me struggling, as my colleague had gone to get help and the restraint. He rushed over to help me. By this time, I had hold of his hands and told him to grab his legs. As this might now get confusing, I will call the 'nutcase' Passenger A and the one who came to help Passenger B.

Passenger A seemed to have superhuman strength and as Passenger B grappled for his legs, Passenger A kicked him in the face. While I was temporarily in shock and distracted, trying to assist Passenger B, Passenger A pushed his fist with all his might into my face and broke my nose. I was in so much pain I could barely breathe, let alone scream. Both Passenger B and I were now bleeding profusely and could barely see through all the blood. However, punching me in the nose had surprisingly positive results, as I felt so much pain when my nose broke, I dug my well-manicured nails right through the flesh of his arm.

This resulted in him screaming like Liza Minnelli on acid — don't really know how that sounds but it seemed the right description — and he momentarily released his vice-like grip on the door handle. It was at that moment, still unable to see, that I felt a cold pair of handcuffs being shoved into my hand. By now, we were past caring about anyone hearing us and the rest of the crew were keeping inquisitive passengers away, as they had either woken up or realised the inflight entertainment on this particular flight was better in the galley than what they were getting on their screens.

With the help of another crew member and Passenger B, we wrestled him to the ground and handcuffed him, albeit not quite to the airline-approved standard to which we had been trained. But restrained he was and we moved him away from the door.

Life on a Postcard No. 55
The Mummy

I don't remember much after that. Just as well, as apparently, I looked like the loser of an Ali fight.

I woke the next day in hospital surrounded by doctors, nurses and my parents. The hospital staff smiled sympathetically at me. Father, as usual, kept his upper lip stiff but Mother's face said it all: she looked like she was constipated, had trapped wind and piles all at the same time. That was not a good look and it worried me. I asked to see a mirror. They discouraged it. They showed me newspapers instead, telling me there was complete media frenzy surrounding the incident. The story had glamour, suspense, excitement, redemption and above all, a happy ending. I was on the front page of every newspaper.

I still asked to see a mirror. I was eventually given one and looked at my reflection with dread and anticipation. I couldn't see a thing. My whole face was mummified and all I could see were the slits for my eyes. I felt my face and although my nose was still there, it was heavily padded.

The doctor examined my reflexes and declared I was 'okay'. Everyone sighed huge sighs of relief and were asked to leave me alone for now. I did mention I felt very lucky as I was in absolutely no pain. The doctor assured me that was because I was on enough morphine to kill a herd of elephants.

That did not sound too good, but at the time I was too drugged to realise it.

The very next day at 9 a.m., my door was flung open and in rushed Gayem, flustered and more dramatic than I had ever seen him before. He was swiftly followed by Mum and Dad, trying to calm him down and virtually restrain him.

"'Aaaaaaggghhhh! You look dreadful Char! You look awful! Your face is probably all mangled under there!" were his opening words to me.

"They wouldn't let me see you yesterday. Only family they said. I was so upset. They only let me in today as Mama Baxter told them that I was virtually family. I have been so worried. I couldn't sleep last night. I got here and there were press everywhere. They were asking *me* questions: how did I know you? Oh, I was so confused. I didn't know whether to talk to them or not. When I heard…"

I put up my hand to stop him. "Would you like to know how I am feeling?" I interjected.

"Yes, of course, but just let me tell you…" Well at least he distracted me from the mundane routine of the hospital.

He was mid-flow when in walked Freya. She was a sight for sore eyes and my eyes were actually sore. She took one look at me and without blinking said, "Well, I guess you could say, "You should see the other guy" but I can't even see you, so can't really tell who is worse off. My guess is, you are. I think I got away easy with my breast removal."

That, of course, made me feel a whole lot better! In her usual throwaway manner Freya made me realise, shit happens, deal with it.

Mother received a message from Alicia to say she would love to fly over to see me but Tris had gone somewhere in Canada and left her to look after the children, as she has yet again lost another nanny. None stayed with her. She went through nannies like Zsa Zsa went through husbands. However, she did send me a message: Was I aware that Channel had stopped making her favourite shade of lipstick?

Mr Raju called and had given Mum a long list of things to get to put in my room, among other things: a plant called Tulsi, a statue of Sai Baba and a glass filled with water in which she needed to place a lemon. Mother was fuming. The Modis called and were very concerned.

Over the next few days, my parents, Gayem, Freya, friends and family visited all the time and I was besieged with requests for interviews from the media. A photograph of my mummified face was circulated across Fleet Street and headlines such as 'Don't Mess with the Mummy', kept me amused for a few days.

The media and the airline begged me to give a press conference from my hospital bed, as in the PR department's words, 'We can't *buy* this publicity, so let's milk it for all we can, for as long as we can'.

The story wouldn't go away and bets were placed as to what my face would look like when they took off the bandages. The airline played on this by purposely not allowing any photographs of me to be published *before* my face had been rearranged by Passenger A.

I finally agreed to talk to the press and was wheeled in my bed to a large auditorium in the hospital, where lectures were usually conducted. There, in front of the world's media, I spoke. They hung on my every word and clicked their cameras, even though they could not see my face.

Overnight, I was the darling of the media. Headlines such as 'THE FACELESS VOICE', 'NOT JUST A PRETTY FACE' and 'TEA, COFFEE OR HANDCUFFS?' were splashed over the papers and television news. I suspect it was also the answers I gave to questions that helped in some way, to catapult me to a worldwide sensation through the circus arena of the media.

Media: "What were you thinking when he grabbed the door handle?"

Me: "I thought to myself, why can't he just contact customer service like everyone else if he doesn't like the food?"

Media: "How did you react when he punched you in the nose?"

Me: "At least I don't have to pay for that expensive nose job I was planning to have."

Media: "What was going through your mind when you finally wrestled him to the ground and got the handcuffs on him?"

Me: "I thought to myself, there has *got* to be an easier way to meet men."

Media: "How much damage do you think you did to his arm?"

Me: "Well, I broke a nail when I dug it into his arm and I would like to see how he explains *those* scratch marks to his wife!"

Passenger A was apparently getting treatment for his anxiety and panic attacks but had been banned from flying with any airline until declared fit by a psychiatrist. He was very apologetic and expressed a desire to visit me in hospital, but was denied the right to see me. I think he was secretly relieved.

I also read about passenger B in the newspapers. He was mummified as well and had been getting his fair share of press attention. He had also been interviewed but in a much more understated manner. I happened to be reading about him one day when one of the nurses came, to give me my daily cocktail of drugs.

"He's only a few doors down, you know," she said. "You should go and visit him."

I was now able to walk and was starting physiotherapy, 'Just to get everything moving again'. My body still ached from the trauma and stress of restraining Passenger A and I was sure Passenger B was in the same situation.

I knew his name was Guillaume and that he was from Paris. "The problem is," he later told me, "my name is not spelt how it is pronounced and not pronounced how it is spelt."

Once the nurse had left, I walked to his room and knocked gently on the door. "Entrez," he mumbled. I walked in and looked at him. It was like looking into a mirror! As soon as we saw each other, we burst into fits of laughter! We had identical mummified faces, clearly bandaged by the same nurse.

I started with, "I never did get a chance to thank you for helping me. I'm not quite sure what I would have done if you hadn't come into the galley at that very moment."

"It is fate, *non*?" he said, in a strong French accent. All of a sudden, I felt a familiar feeling. I felt I was going to swoon. I didn't know if it was his voice or the drugs but I hadn't had this feeling in many years.

We didn't stop talking and laughing till I was thrown out of his room that night, in order for us both to get some rest.

From then on, we were inseparable. We did our physio together, we drank from our straws together, sucked soup through our tubes together, took our IV drips together.

The first thing I fell in love with, as clearly, I could not see his face, was his accent. I would pop my head into his room each morning and start by saying, "Guillaume, say oranges," and he would say 'oranges' in the most amazing French accent and I would melt.

He was a freelance travel photographer, who travelled the world taking photographs of anything. His job sounded romantic, exotic and exciting but he said that, as with anything, it was also a lot of hard work. "I go where the work is and no job is too big or too small."

He called me '*mon gros bébé*' and I knew I had only felt something like this once before. Was the ghost finally being put to rest? Was I finally healing? Did it have to take a huge physical trauma to wipe out the mental one I had been carrying around with me?

Guillaume and I were symbiotic. We seemed to fit well together. We spoke about our pasts and though I did talk to him about Zaheer and told him all the gory details, I had left out my depth of feelings for him and glossed over the part that made me feel that somewhere, something deep inside me had died and that nothing could bring that back. We spoke about our futures and our future together.

We were already in love when they told Guillaume he could have his bandages off three and half weeks later. However, he refused. He said he wanted to keep his on till I was ready to have mine removed. Such a romantic gesture did not go unnoticed by anyone. By now the media had picked up on our romance and were going wild. They called us 'Mr and Mrs Mummy' and even cornier names than that. The airline was still milking me, the publicity cow and by now, I have to say my nipples were quite raw from all the milking but even I could not deny them and everyone else, this one last fanfare.

Finally, four weeks after we'd arrived in hospital and half

a week overdue for Guillaume, we were now both ready. We agreed to have one television station and one newspaper reporter in the room when the unveiling took place. In true movie blockbuster style, we sat opposite each other and they began to reveal our faces.

As the bandages came off, the relief was so great I sounded like Meg Ryan in *When Harry met Sally*.

Once again, cameras clicked away as finally our faces were revealed. I'm not sure what either of us or anyone else was expecting — a movie scene this was not. We both still looked like our faces had been trampled over by a herd of rhino, on a stampede to get the last dandelion of the season.

Someone said, "You may now kiss the Mummy" and we obliged with a quick kiss.

After a while, once they had exploited us to the full and realised we were quite normal people in the cold light of day, the media frenzy died out.

However, sadly, I had to leave the airline as Mother's blood pressure could not take it and with all my media exposure, I had secured an interesting job as a daily columnist for a popular national newspaper and had a long list of magazines requesting articles from me, on anything from safety in the skies to comfortable clothes for travelling and being restrained in, to colonic irrigation. I was thoroughly enjoying this new career, Guillaume was busier than ever and sometimes I accompanied him on his trips.

Life on a Postcard No. 56
Unique by A Thousand Miles

Dear Mother,

(As you can see the 'Dear Mother' postcards continued even though I had left the airline and was now a mere passenger when I travelled with Guillaume. But yet Mother still expected a postcard each time.)

As the slogan of the Seychelles suggests, there is so much of this island that really is unique. It is one of the most beautiful islands I have ever been to and you know how many islands I have visited. Mahe itself, where you arrive and where the capital Victoria is located is great fun.

The first day we were there, Guillaume took me to one of the islands where he was photographing something very unusual. It was magical. The island was called Praslin and I lost myself in the Valle De Mer, an untouched forest that sheltered hundreds and thousands of Coco de Mer trees. Not a single leaf on a single tree could be taken, unless the person had a permit from the Government to do so. The trees were left to grow at will and were never cut or pruned. The often-repeated story of this plant was an interesting one.

No one knows how this coconut tree reproduces. There is no evidence to show that any kind of pollination takes place. Endemic to the Seychelles, the Coco de Mer has a male and female plant. The male plant quite strikingly resembles the human male reproductive organ. (Though some men may disagree!) Now Mother, stop blushing.

The female Coco de Mer resembles the female reproductive anatomy.

The Seychellois believe (and they have convinced a fair few tourists), that this plant reproduces by mating. Looking at the distance between the male and female trees, you may need a lot of convincing! Once the female Coco de Mer coconut has dried, its 'likeness to the female anatomy is even more striking'. This dried coconut can be bought and taken out of the country with a not so easily or cheaply available export license.

Due to his connections and persuasion skills, Guillaume bought us one to bring back home! I can't believe it! It is going to be the talking piece of all our parties! You can borrow it sometime, Mother.

The next day, we travelled by light aircraft to another one of the many Seychelles islands; my heaven on earth, Bird Island. As our big bird touched down on the island, the small birds took off from their trees.

It was these small birds that Guillaume had been asked to photograph and something again that was quite unique to this island — the Stooty Terns.

During the months of May to October, three million Sooty Terns nested there. During the rest of the year however, there were only eight to ten thousand of them!

The aquamarine blues and greens of the Indian ocean were breath-taking and we snorkelled and swam, listening to the sounds of the Sootys, as well as numerous other types of birds and the sound of the ocean hitting the rocks.

The chalets were unbelievable, tastefully decorated and beautiful. While we ate our scrumptious dinner, our room was transformed: the mosquito net was drawn over our four-poster bed, the bed clothes were turned down and an insect repellent was left burning.

By night, however, Bird Island was no place for the cockroach- and insect-fearing.

Mum, I really do need to bring you here.

Life on a Postcard No. 57
Er We Are Family Now

Having first met G's family during our stay in hospital and having got to know them, I fell in love with them as well.

His sister Nicole was a true force of nature, funny and fiery at the same time. She was an artist in the true form and painted pictures. She didn't draw squares around squares or cut up fish and encase them in formaldehyde and she didn't make or unmake beds — though she did do a mock, unmade bed for us in the hospital with bedpans and water jugs, which was hilarious. You had to be there. However, her 'day job' was as a jewellery designer for a very upmarket jewellery store.

She loved her name until the early 1990s when due to the Renault Clio ad, she was plagued with 'Ni-coooole and Papa'. Being French of course, she called her father 'Papa' and therefore family and friends alike thought it was hilarious to re-enact the ad, each time they met. She thought it was funny the first time and then from the second time onwards, she hated it.

She was married to an Italian called Harry. Yes, Harry. His parents were huge Clint Eastwood and *Dirty Harry* fans and he'd been brought up on the movies.

They were only a few years younger than us but had been married a while and fought constantly. There was no doubt they loved each other but everyone put their arguing down to the temperaments of the two cultures and left it at that. G's parents hated them arguing but G and I used to bring out the popcorn and found it more entertaining than any fast-paced thriller. The arguments were always about the most mundane things that they managed to turn into exciting and interesting topics.

Nicole: "I told you to bring me some pumpkin, so I could make some soup."

Harry: "Well, there was no pumpkin, so I brought you the next best thing."

Nicole: "You brought me pumpkin seeds! What the bloody hell do you want me to do with those? Stick them in the ground and wait for them to grow before I make pumpkin soup?"

Harry: "Well, you do the shopping next time then. I'm telling you there was no pumpkin."

Nicole: "There *is* pumpkin as large as anything between the swede and the squash."

Harry: "What the bloody hell is swede?"

Nicole: "Aaaaggghh! I can't rely on you for anything! What good are you? Why don't you go back to Italy and maybe women will tolerate this incompetence there?"

Harry now moved in for the kill, a move that was guaranteed to end any verbal argument and take it to the next level — violence.

Harry: "Ni-cooooolle?"

Nicole lunged at him with the wooden chair she was standing next to and chased him around the room.

How could we not enjoy such *joie de vivre*!

Guillaume's father, Alain, was a mathematician and travelled the world giving lectures, taking classes and was a visiting professor at most of the universities around the world. His mother, Hélène, was a very stylish dress designer. "Aren't they all?" Mother said, when she heard.

They both spoke perfect English. Mother didn't speak any French and although Father liked to think he spoke it beautifully, that was far from the truth. I had a smattering but carried on speaking regardless, as I didn't care!

Life on a Postcard No. 58
The Reunion

It had been a while since we had met. When I say *we*, I mean Freya, Adrian, Gaymen and me. What with me being in hospital and all the commotion about that, with Freya getting her Double Ds and with Gaymen involved with yet another drama to do with Truly Scrumptious, we started calling ourselves 'We Four', like our Queen's father had done before he became king. We weren't exactly royalty but we did have a queen among us. We were celebrating my recovery, Freya's Double Ds and the fact that she had just been given the all-clear. We were just about to tuck into some starters when Nicole called. She and I had become very close, very quickly. She called me for advice and I called her for entertainment. She was one of the funniest people I knew. This time it was the former.

"That's it!" she said. "This time I am absolutely divorcing him! I am fed up, I have had it. I can't stand it *any* longer. He is completely useless!" she ranted.

"Do you know what he has done this time? He used half a bottle of gin to light a fire! Why, you ask? Because he wanted to get it over and done with quickly, if you please and the bottle of gin was the closest thing he could find, to ignite a fire at great speed. Can you believe that? The alcohol spread and has burnt half the bushes in our garden and now the neighbours are complaining, as they are worried their trees are going to catch fire and we still can't put the fire out, so now we have to call the fire brigade! That's it. I've had it."

As I was talking to her, I looked across at Freya. There she was, pushing her great big Double D's into Adrian's face and fooling around. What she had gone through, no young lady should go through. Yet she did it with bravery, was stoic, never batted an eyelid, never complained, never felt sorry for herself and just took it all in her stride. It was just another thing that happened to her. That was it.

This time as homage to her, I decided to use the Freya style of advice: truth and brevity."

Me: "Nicole, do you love him?"
Nicole: "Yes."
Me: "Nicole, does he love you?"
Nicole: "Yes."
Me: "Nicole, can you talk to him and sort it out?"
Nicole: "I guess so."
Me: "Right now, standing where you are, right at this moment, can you imagine your life without him?"
Nicole: "No."
Me: "So, are you really thinking of divorcing him?"
Nicole: "Oh, Charlotte, you always know the right thing to say!"

And with that, another world war was averted.

Life on a Postcard No. 59
The Heimlich Ring

It was on one of G's trips that I had the opportunity to once again put my cabin crew training into practice. We were on our way to Nassau in the Bahamas, where Guillaume had a seven-day assignment.

Before the meal service, we were handed our menus and I noticed all the cabin crew smirking each time they passed us. I finally couldn't stand it any longer and went into the galley to say, "Yes, I know you recognise me and yes, I'm the girl who tackled the passenger and was famous for a while, so if you would like to ask me any questions, please do so. You don't have to worry about approaching me."

They looked stunned but they nodded and said they would definitely ask me if they had any questions. As I left the galley, I heard them burst into fits of laughter. I sat back down in my seat, puzzled and was about to mention this to Guillaume when he said that the fish pie had been recommended highly by the crew and should he order that for me?

I said I preferred the pasta but he was most insistent I have the fish pie and said he would order the pasta and we could share both dishes. I agreed.

There was more smirking from the crew when they handed me my meal. I again tried to talk to Guillaume about this but he asked me how my fish pie was, making sure he followed each bite that entered my mouth. I was about to tell him that something fishy was going on here (pun clearly intended), when I heard a spluttering and a slapping sound coming from the other side of cabin. I looked over and a woman was furiously slapping the man next to her on the back and I could clearly see he was choking.

I jumped over the seats and was at his side before the crew got to him. As I had started giving him the Heimlich I shouted, "Don't worry, I have done this quite successfully before," by way of reassurance and after only a few thrusts, a large piece of fish flew out of his mouth. We were all about to applaud and rejoice when he sat bolt upright, gulped and said, "I think I swallowed something large and hard!"

I was so tempted to say, "Haven't we all, sir, haven't we all," but somehow didn't think it was terribly appropriate at that time.

He continued. "I think there was something in the fish pie!" All colour drained from the faces of the crew and while still attending to the man, I then began to hear the sound of someone hyperventilating. I looked across the aisle and saw it was Guillaume. I was about to charge over to him when one of the crew, the previously smirky one, said, "Let me speak to him."

She went over to him and started to comfort him, saying, "Don't worry we'll sort it out."

Guillaume had wanted to ask me to marry him in a novel and interesting way. He'd convinced the airline to bake the ring into my fish pie. The only problem was, they had labelled the wrong one and the poor sod who got it, was of course least expecting it and choked on it. I had obviously helped extract the piece of fish it was buried in but for reasons we will never know, the ring had managed to escape and had gone down his gullet!

A diversion was declared, we landed in New York an hour

later and Mr Joyce, with my large engagement ring inside him, was rushed to the nearest hospital, along with his very worried wife who was incandescent with rage.

A worried wife incandescent with rage is not a good combination. Of course, Guillaume and I accompanied them.

"How could you be so stupid?" she said, when we were all safely speeding down the freeway with sirens blaring.

Guillaume could only apologise profusely but also suggested that the airline should take some of the responsibility, for mixing up the fish pies.

Through the wonders of keyhole surgery, the ring was extracted, washed and duly handed to Guillaume. He looked at me and said, "Clearly you would prefer another ring."

I said, "Are you kidding? You couldn't make up an engagement story such as this. Put that on my finger right now!"

When I told my parents that Guillaume and I were engaged and moving in together, they were thrilled but Mother was slightly concerned.

She and Father called a meeting and reverted back to their hand-over-mouth scenarios, whispering and having a conversation about me like I was not there. This time however, they did it all at once.

Mum: "They eat frogs, Anthony dear."

Dad: "No, no. They eat frogs' *legs,* dear."

Mum: "But that's even worse. That means there are poor little frogs trying to hop all over France without any legs?"

Dad: "Don't be completely ridiculous, darling. They don't just cut off their legs and send them on their way."

Mum: "How many years have you been married to me, darling? You should know by now when I am being silly and facetious."

Dad: "Well, it's difficult to tell darling, as your facetiousness cannot easily be distinguished from your indigestion."

I sat there in complete bewilderment, hoping this was not happening, that it was all just a terrible dream and that I would soon wake up.

"They also eat raw garlic," Mother carried on. "Dracula ate raw garlic."

Without realising it, I got caught up in the conversation, sucked into the abyss from which there was very little hope of getting out when they started these conversations.

"No Mum, Dracula was *afraid* of garlic as it turned him into dust. What am I saying? Dracula isn't even real!"

"But Lottie darling, what about the horses, darling?"

"The horses?" I said. "What about the horses?"

"Well, darling, they eat them as well."

Mother and I were both ardent fans of the songwriter Cole Porter. While out riding a horse one day, it threw him off, resulting in him breaking his spine and being paralysed for life. He famously said after that, 'Ten million Frenchmen can't be wrong: you don't ride horses, you eat them.'

There was just no point in talking to Mother, other than to beg her to get some help.

During my hospitalisation and for a time afterwards, my Marvin dreams had ceased. I sort of missed them and was wondering whether that was the end of them and the shock of what happened to me might have blocked any imagination I had developed when dreaming.

Then one night… I had the strangest dream of them all. Marvin the Moose goes to the doctor as he needs to be vaccinated. Again, I put my dream down to the recent medical incident with my engagement ring and left it at that.

Life on a Postcard No. 60
So, This Is What They Call Closure

Soon after we got engaged, Guillaume broached the subject of visiting India. He had been there many times on photograph assignments but never to Hyderabad and wanted to go there with me, as it had been such a huge part of my life and because I talked about it so much. He was keen to meet the Mr Raju he had heard so much about.

Mr Raju yet again, met us at the airport. He had always been there for me whenever I needed him. Without a fuss and without drama. But the one thing he always felt strongly about was that I should meet the Modi's because 'ignoring it is not the answer'. Yet again, as soon as we met at the airport, he started to speak and saw my face closed to any suggestion, even now, of meeting the Modis.

Strangely, I didn't have any feelings one way or another on arriving in India. It felt like a lifetime ago. So much had happened and I was at a different place in my life. I was pleased to be there but I didn't want to revisit the past.

A day or so after we arrived, we accompanied Mr Raju to the supermarket and I began to fill my trolley with all my favourite Indian treats: *chudwa, mithai, chikki,* spiced chai tea.

As I walked down one of the aisles, from the corner of my eye I noticed a lady who looked familiar. She looked haggard but still very elegant, immaculately turned out and yet she had sad, tired eyes. For a moment I couldn't place her. Then my blood ran cold. I darted across the supermarket, abandoning my trolley in the middle of the aisle just as she noticed me and was about to speak. I shouted to Mr Raju we had to leave right now.

On leaving the supermarket, I flew into the car and shut the door. I could see the lady rushing towards me, quickly followed by Mr Raju and Guillaume in the distance. I turned away but she was soon at the car door. I jumped when she started banging on the window but refused to open it.

She then started thumping on the door with tears pouring down her face, in full view of everyone in the street. Mrs Modi, the most dignified, classy, elegant wife of a General was now screaming, "Why won't you talk to us? You *have* to talk to us!"

An hour later, I was sitting in their lounge without Mr Raju or Guillaume. The General, Mrs Modi and I all had mugs of tea, cupped in our hands and for a few moments, we sat in silence. Then that silence was broken by a soft sobbing. I looked up but couldn't see where it was coming from. I looked at the General and Mrs Modi. Their faces were solemn but they weren't sobbing. They were just looking straight at me. The soft sobbing then became louder and louder till I realised it was me.

After a few minutes, the sobbing turning into wailing. By this time, they were both at my side crying as well but I realised they were not crying for Zaheer, or for themselves — they were crying for me.

They had done their grieving. They had faced the reality that he was gone. They had had to. I did not. I had been able to run away and that is exactly what I'd done. I hadn't said goodbye, I hadn't truly accepted it had happened. There had been no closure. The wound had not healed; it had merely formed a thin scab.

I begged them to forgive me for being so selfish, for constantly shunning their requests to talk or to meet.

We talked about everything from his death to his life, to his passion for living and feeling.

It was there, five years after his death I finally felt it was okay to let go. It was okay to move on. At last, I could. They could not, but in some way felt I was being given permission to be happy again. They said Zaheer would have wanted me to be happy again, even though they could not be.

I did move on and did so largely due to his mother's parting words to me that day, which helped greatly in giving me a reason for his death. What she said to me will remain with me for the rest of my life.

"You know, Charlotte, every day I remind myself that he was so amazing, so wonderful. He was too good for this world, Charlotte and therefore he had to leave it. He was too good for this world and therefore could not live in it. He was just too good for this world."

A week later, after Guillaume had been shown around Hyderabad, Mr Raju dropped us at the airport. Before we boarded the plane, he took me to one side and said, "Now, Charlottie, you be happy now. No harm will come to you and you will have a happy and healthy life."

I thanked him but told him that as much as I admired him, not even he could see into the future and having experienced one tragedy, I was of the opinion that anything could happen, at any time. He said, "No, it will not."

"How can you be so sure?" I enquired.

"Because everything else he told you came true," Mr Raju said.

I looked at him confused.

"Don't you remember the jotish?" Mr Raju said. He looked as me as I recalled. "You will travel a lot. You will have one tragedy in your life and then your life will be smooth."

"Yes!" I said, "I *do* remember!"

"And was he not right?"

"Yes, he was, I suppose," I said. "Oh, my goodness, he said I would have three sons as well!"

"You see, you are blessed from now on."

I couldn't possibly explain to poor Mr Raju that for me, three sons would certainly not be a blessing.

Life on a Postcard No. 61
How Many Words Does That Make?

No sooner had I arrived back from India when Freya called. "I need to talk to you."

Freya *never* needed to talk to you. Everyone else always needed to talk to Freya but Freya never needed to talk to anyone.

My head was spinning. "Is… is… the cancer back?" I asked, hesitantly.

"No, don't be silly. Come over now."

I had barely walked into the door when she said, "We've split up." I had learnt something from Freya, so instead of reacting how I normally would, possibly with a combination of shock and curiosity and support, I said, "Well, I can't say I blame him. Look at this place — it constantly looks like Tracey Emins' unmade bed."

"That's not it," she said with a straight face, knowing I was being sarcastic but ignoring it. I could now see she was visibly shaken.

Apparently, Adrian had waited for her to get the all-clear to talk to her. He loved her more than he had loved anyone and could not imagine his life without her. And for that reason, it hurt him more than ever: each time she snubbed his affection, each time he told her he loved her and she virtually ignored him and each time he showered love, attention, thoughtfulness and romance on her and she never returned it. Each time a bit of him died inside. For him, knowing she loved him was not enough. He needed her to show him.

"And you know me, Charlotte. I don't do romance, I get claustrophobic when someone is too tactile, I don't show my affection even though I feel it. I can't do mushy."

I walked slowly over to her, grabbed her shoulders and started to shake her vigorously and yelled, "Well, you are going to do it now! You are going to do mushy with the mushiest mush, you are going to do romance, you are going to do tactile and you are going to do love and attention!"

Through her shaky voice I heard her say, "Ddddooonnnn'ttt sssshhhaaakkkke the lllleeefffttt one. You can shake the right one! The left one hasn't settled yet!" I stopped shaking her, quickly withdrew and looked at her breasts in horror. She grabbed hold of them to make sure they were still in the same place. "I have to be careful till they settle," she said

We spent the day thinking, discussing, scheming, plotting, planning, shopping and executing what we were going to do.

That evening, she called Adrian and asked to see him at his flat. She walked in through the door in the sexiest, black, lace dress you had ever seen. She started to unbutton the top of the dress, specially chosen and bought for its buttons all the way down the front. As she revealed her chest, on it was written, I CAN'T LIVE WITHOUT YOU. I LOVE YOU. (This would have never been possible pre-cancer as her chest would not have been big enough to hold all the words. But thanks to her Double Ds we managed to fit all the words in perfectly.) She then slipped off her bra and around her nipples we had written 'ADRIAN' in all the colours of the rainbow.

She continued to unbutton her dress and just above the navel were the words: WILL YOU MARRY ME? And in her navel was a gold wedding band.

Freya dropped to her knees, popped the ring out of her navel and slipped it onto his finger. I don't think there was a happier man in all of Great Britain that night.

It might have been the excitement of the proposal that brought on another Marvin dream. This time, he spent ages doing the housework and got sucked up by a giant Hoover.

Life on a Postcard No. 62
What in God's Name Am I Going to Do Now?

Having been to India, G now wanted to take me to Nairobi, Africa, not only because he loved the country and had been on many assignments there but also, a friend and fellow photographer who happened to be British, had set down roots there and started a wildlife park and animal hospital, to care for sick and injured animals. He was also going to be G's best man.

I had heard about Andrew Marshall constantly and if G hadn't been so in love with me, I would have had no hesitation in saying he was in love with Andrew.

"Andrew is amazing. Do you know he learnt to fly a plane in Africa because he had to transport some sick animals?"

"Andrew is such a wonderful photographer. Look at this photograph he took of a whale skimming the waves. I could never take a photograph like that." "Andrew is so good with animals. He can virtually talk to them and they understand him."

Therefore, I was not looking forward to this meeting at all, as I did not want to have to worship at the shrine of Andrew for a week but it had to be done. G had been keen to see and experience my past, so I had to muster up the enthusiasm to experience his past with Andrew, the 'global warrior', the healer of all beings.

On disembarking from the aeroplane, I saw G's face light

up and his face broke into one of the broadest smiles I had ever seen. I followed his gaze and as I watched this figure walking towards us, something felt very familiar to me. I couldn't quite put my finger on it but then it struck me: what I was experiencing were familiar physical symptoms from when I was a teenager and a young boy had grabbed my arm and rescued me from wetting myself.

As Andrew walked towards us, everything around me moved at a normal pace but as I watched him approach, he slowed down and all I could see was him gliding towards us in slow motion, his dark glasses hiding part of his weather-worn face. Apologies for the clichéd description.

His white tee-shirt covered a muscular pair of shoulders and his long shorts ended short of his Jesus sandals. I felt something deep in the pit of my stomach. Was it the airline food? Had my parents been right? Had it finally caught up with me and now I was going to die from it? I wasn't quite sure but I knew it was a dangerous feeling.

He finally reached us, grabbed G's hand with all the vigour of someone about to arm wrestle, then he wrapped his arm around G's neck with all the enthusiasm and strength of a python grabbing his kill. Well, we were in Africa and it would have been terribly inappropriate of me not to use a wildlife analogy!

This was clearly not a man who did things by halves.

Andrew Marshall had never married. 'He's just not the marrying type,' G had once told me. 'He's too busy saving the world and taking care of other things to think of himself.'

I tried to size him up without blushing. He was a good ten years older than G and had an air about him that I had never seen before: a confidence and look that said, 'I can do anything. I am capable of anything.'

We boarded what could only loosely have been called a 'jeep'. It barely had doors and certainly no windows or a roof. There was a frame you had to duck under to get into the car and it was my guess, that was what was keeping the whole contraption together. We piled in and as we started the journey, I remember thinking, 'Well, this isn't too bad', as the roads were lovely and wide and certainly better than our potholed ones back home.

Then, we turned off the main road and started to trundle down a very rocky path. I use the word 'path' loosely; a more appropriate word for it would be 'dirt track'.

I don't think the wheels of the jeep even touched the path, sorry, dirt track more than a couple of times, as we were thrown from side to side. All the time, Andrew kept talking to G about the elephant he had rescued from poachers and how he had managed to catch the poachers this time but how they always got away, as their network of bribes reached even the highest authorities and so on. Every now and again, he would glance back at me. I felt the blood rush to my face each time he did that and tried to look casual and smile. He told me later, he was only doing that to check I was still there. Many a time he had lost a passenger on the road, leading up to his animal sanctuary.

I could see the look in G's eyes as his hero waffled on and on about life in Africa, about how much he would have loved G to join him here but now that he had gone over to the 'dark side' and was getting hitched, it wouldn't be possible. he needed to have words with me for taking G away from him.

When we finally arrived, my bottom felt it had been punished with twenty lashes and my teeth were still rattling. When Andrew put out his hand to help me off the jeep, I was tingling all over and again I could not tell you whether that was because of the way he made me feel or whether it was because of the ride.

He led us into his den and I was pleasantly surprised as to how well furnished and spotlessly clean this house was, especially as it was practically in the middle of the jungle. *I mean, who would come to work here*? was my first thought.

Then I realised there was a little commune around the house, with the animal conservationists and people that worked with Andrew, who lived in other little makeshift houses around the main house.

The sun was now beginning to set and I started to hear grasshoppers and other insects start their dusk chorus. It was music to my ears. Of the many times I came to Africa and the few times I had been on safari, this was the sound I loved the most.

G made sure Andrew knew what an animal lover I was and how I had been to Africa and on safari. Andrew asked politely about my experiences and when I told him about my giraffe incident, he seemed quite impressed, which pleased me no end. He said, "So, what we have here is a girl with no fear of wild animals."

When I thought about it, I realised I actually had no fear at all of any animal. Andrew said that was dangerous. He explained that in all his years of dealing with animals, he not only respected them but respectfully feared them as well. He said without that sense of fear, he would not be here today. "You have to know when you hold them, know when you fold them, know when to walk away and know when to run," he quoted from country singer, Kenny Williams' song 'The Gambler'. He and G laughed at this. How was that appropriate? I asked myself but knew what he meant.

Life on a Postcard No. 63
Warning: Cliché Overload!

That night, we all sat around the campfire and ate yams and other steamed vegetables to the soft humming of African songs. Each time I glanced at Andrew through the flames as he sat opposite me, he was looking straight at me. His piercing, crystal-blue eyes stared at me, making me feel like he was looking into the depths of my soul. It made me shiver. It was liberating and nerve-wracking at the same time. G stayed up talking to Andrew well into the night and I fell asleep under a mosquito net, on our very low but comfortable bed in the guest room.

It was 3 a.m. when I got up to get a glass of water. I wandered into the kitchen area and opened the fridge door. I jumped and let out a little shriek, when I saw the silhouette of a half-naked man standing next to me. I opened the door further to see who it was and he said, "You felt it too, didn't you?"

Andrew's eyes were still piercing and still staring. "What do you mean?" I said, knowing full well what he meant.

"You and I, we have something in common. We both have a dangerous side that no one else understands; we both want it all and we want it now. We want to be conventional but we want to walk on the wild side. We want all the trappings but we also want to be free. I saw that in you as soon as I met you."

Where the hell did that come from? I thought.

"Well, from where I'm standing, we are polar opposites,"

I said, keeping up the pace. "You're the dangerous one, I'm conventional. You walk on the wild side and want to be free and I want all the trappings."

"Yes, but that's on the surface. Underneath, you have a burning desire to scream from the rooftops and be free. You've convinced yourself you need the trappings but your heart knows you want to run wild."

"You think you know me but what do you really know about me?" I asked. This man had literally got into my soul, he had spread all the layers apart as he went further down and got to the very core of my being and was now ripping it all apart and throwing it in my face. How could he do that after meeting me barely twelve hours earlier?

I wanted to punch him and jump on him and rip his clothes off all at the same time. As I couldn't decide which was the stronger desire, I did nothing. Plus, there wouldn't be much to rip off as all he had on was a very flimsy pair of shorts.

Before I could do or say anything else, he dragged me to him and kissed me. I couldn't pull away. I kept thinking I should but couldn't. Finally, we had to come up for air. Panting hard, we stood staring at each other and a second later we came together again, unable to control ourselves.

Finally, sense prevailed and I ran back to my room.

The first opportunity we got to talk the next day was when G had got up early, to photograph the rescued elephant. We were to follow later.

Me: "How could you do this to your best friend?"

Andrew: "What do you mean *me*? What about you? How could you do this to your fiancé? I'll tell you why we did it. It's because our strength of feeling is so intense and we can't control it. If we could, we would have. I have never felt like this before."

Me: "Really? I find that hard to believe; hard to believe that you meet me for the first time and all of a sudden you can't keep your hands off me."

Andrew: "I have seen you many times before this and fell in love with you the first time I saw you."

Me: "What do you mean?"

Andrew: "G has sent me numerous photographs and videos of you."

With that, Andrew rattled off videos he had watched of me, what I was wearing and gave me details of what I was doing. It was quite shocking to hear what he was saying, as I never thought someone like him would pay that much attention, to what a person was wearing or doing.

It wasn't just shocking and flattering but attracted me to him even more than ever and that was dangerous.

As we had to leave to meet G, we had to end the conversation there. As we approached the enclosure where the elephant was being cared for, I noticed Eli the elephant had a baby as well! We were not permitted inside as the animals were wary of people but I could feed the baby through an opening. She was adorable. When she finished her milk bottle, she moved over to where G was standing. He was drinking a Coke. She reached through the opening and gently took the Coke bottle off him with her trunk and proceeded to knock it back! Andrew told us they'd discovered she liked Coke when her carer had been drinking a bottle the other day and had left it on the side. She picked it up, tried it and liked it. She wasn't allowed too many though!

The rest of the week was agonising and we exchanged many sideways glances. I knew he wanted to get me alone. I avoided getting up in the middle of the night and stayed well away from his room. On the last night, I decided we need to talk about it. After G had gone to bed, I hovered around the fridge, pretending to make a cup of tea. Soon enough, Andrew emerged. He was smiling. He came over to me, fully expecting me to respond to his advances. I drew away.

"What happened the first night has to be forgotten. I love G with all my heart and I should have never given into my urges the way I did. It was a fleeting moment of craziness and we have to forget it ever happened."

"I can't ever forget it," Andrew said. "I have wanted you from the first time I clapped eyes on you and will always want you." How often did one hear that from a 'global warrior'? Yes, it was romantic, yes it was sweeping-me-off-my-feet stuff but by now, my feet were firmly planted on the ground and they were not budging.

"I'm not going to fall for this kind of talk, when I know the moment I leave the next little thing in a skirt will take up all your attention."

Andrew looked genuinely hurt by that remark. I couldn't tell whether he really was though. This was the thing about global warriors who went around saving the world and who were deadly attractive and made women swoon: I just couldn't tell if he was genuine.

Me: "I don't know how you're going to stand next to him with a straight face, as his best man, if you don't tell him what happened the other night."

Andrew: "Nothing happened, Charlotte."

Me: "Oh, so it was nothing then?" (Typical female response)

Andrew: "He... What I mean is, you have nothing to be

ashamed about. We were attracted to each other, that attraction was too much for us to resist. We kissed. That's all. What we should be proud of was that we didn't take it any further and both stopped before it was too late, as we both love G very much."

For a moment that made sense. However, I managed to shake off the fake logic fairly quickly.

Me: "No. I will have to tell him in order to move on and marry him. If he feels he can't trust me, then so be it but I can't marry him without being completely honest."

Andrew: "You're being silly now. What he doesn't know can't hurt him. You will only hurt him and not gain anything at all."

Even standing next to him, my legs were ready to give way. Being so close to him was torture, but I kept telling myself that what I was feeling was all part of the magic, the country, the wilderness, the animals and my romantic notions.

Andrew suggested we meet when he was back in England a month later. I declined.

On the flight back home, I wanted to tell G what had happened. I tried to several times but couldn't do it. How weak could I be? I loved this man but then why had I done what I'd done and what kind of friend was Andrew, to do what he did?

Out of exhaustion, I fell asleep and had another one of my Marvin dreams.

This time, Marvin went to a museum and inadvertently defaced an expensive piece of art.

I put the dream down to either my guilty conscience or the fact that I had been around animals for the past week. But then I should have been dreaming of wild animals, not a stuffed toy that I have constantly pretended is a real living thing.

Freud, where are you when I need my dreams interpreted?

Life on a Postcard No. 64
Should I? Shouldn't I?

Once home, tormented and traumatised by my guilt, I turned to Gayem. Freya was away and I wanted to wait till I saw her face to face, to ask her opinion.

When I told him what had happened in Nairobi, he said, "How could you, Char! You have betrayed G and yourself!" Why did gay friends never behave the way you wanted them to? Why did they never live up to the stereotypes? It was very inconvenient.

"But Gayem, I thought you would understand as *you* are attracted to one man after another. Why should it be different for me?"

"Because I'm not engaged to another man," he said, indignantly

"What should I do? I'm in such a quandary," I said.

"Well, you can't marry him without him knowing the truth," Gaymen said and that was that, as far as he was concerned.

Gayem was very annoying, just like Freya. He always told me what I didn't want to hear, even though I knew it was the right thing.

Finally, Freya came back.

Me: "What shall I do, Frey? I'm tormented by this."

Freya: "Do you want to tell him?" (Why was she so annoying all the time? Especially when I wanted her to take responsibility for what I was about to do, she put the responsibility and accountability squarely back on my shoulders.)

Me: "Yes I do but I'm afraid I'll lose him and he won't want to marry me."

Freya: "So what's the worst that can happen?"

Me: "Er… I think I just told you: I will lose him and he won't want to marry me?"

Freya: "Is that the worst that could happen?"

Me: "Yes, in this situation. Yes, that is the worst that could happen."

Freya: "Really? Then you're very lucky."

Me: "Well, should I tell him or should I not?"

Freya: "Whether you tell him or not, whatever choice you make, there will be consequences. However, only you can make that choice."

Well, she was as useful as waterproofs in a tornado.

Life on a Postcard No. 65
The Truth Will Set You Free

I knew I had to tell G sooner rather than later. I knew in my heart of hearts I had to tell him but I was scared; scared he wouldn't want to marry me or in the best-case scenario, he would want to postpone the wedding, to think about how we could move on from there. I wanted reassurance that everything was going to be all right.

The only person in the world I could call on for that, was Mr Raju. He always made me feel safe, made me feel like what was meant to be would be and that who were we to change the path written out for us.

"Mr Raju," I said.

"Yes, my dear Charlottie?" he said, almost as if he knew why I was calling him.

"I have done a terrible thing and now I have to put it right."

"This terrible thing you have done, is it you have taken someone's life?"

"What? No, of course not!"

"Then anything else we can deal with. What you have done, can it be undone?"

"No," I said, "it cannot. And when I tell the truth it will hurt."

"Do you regret it?"

"Yes of course, terribly."

"Do you see where you went wrong?"

"Yes, I do."

"Then tell the truth, Charlottie, because even the most painful truth is less painful and less harmful than a lie. If you do the right thing, then that could correct the wrong but if you continue to do the wrong thing, there is no hope."

Yet again, not only had Mr Raju put my problem into perspective, he had reassured me that the path I was about to take was the right one.

Life on a Postcard No. 66
A Deal in Deal

I told G I needed to talk to him before the wedding plans were afoot. He smiled at me almost knowingly and said, "Why don't we go to Deal?"

"What? Where's that?" I had never heard of this delightful little seaside town in Kent.

"Before all the wedding hullabaloo." (G loved that word and was fascinated by the English language — he used that word quite a lot and usually it annoyed me terribly, as he tried to bring it in in most conversations.)

This time it didn't bother me, as I just wanted to get this over and done with.

"Before all the *hullabaloo* of the wedding starts, why don't we go away for a few days?" he repeated.

G had been to Deal for a shoot once and had absolutely fallen in love with this little place. The town was tiny and everything was within walking distance of everything else. On a clear day, if you stood next to Deal Castle you could see France. It might have been that he felt close to home or it might have been the sheer peace and tranquillity one felt, as you entered Deal.

We arrived, unpacked and went for a walk along the stony beach. Seagulls shrieked expectantly as we neared them. Then their shrieks turned to disappointed squawks when they realised, we didn't have any titbits for them.

We sat on the beach and I was very conscious that this was

not a time to get emotional or to start apologising profusely for what I had done. I needed to tell it like it was and let the chips fall where they may.

So without histrionics, I gave G a factual account of what had happened that night. I then explained, I genuinely did not know what had possessed me to act that way as I loved him very much but couldn't lie and that I was attracted to Andrew. I wanted to say that a lot of that was due to the passion G felt for him and the build-up to meeting him and the amazing life he led in Africa, and also, I wanted to say 'who couldn't be attracted to that?' But that would have been a cop out.

G didn't say anything for a bit then he spoke. "'Okay, I can't say I'm not upset but I suspected something like this might happen as I knew Andrew was attracted to you. He told me so when I sent him your photographs. Andrew's like that. He said to me, "Mate, she's gorgeous. Don't leave me alone with her." And when we were there, I knew something was amiss by the way you were behaving around each other. Andrew will never change and I love him for who he is. He has no sense of loyalty as such and takes what he wants. I have no doubt that he was also very attracted to you but living on his own where he does, tends to blur what the rest of us think of as *acceptable* behaviour."

Then he asked the killer question. "How do you feel about him now?"

I thought for a few minutes, wanting to give him an honest answer but not wanting to sound like I was talking to a girlfriend telling her about my first crush. "Well, I won't lie and say I'm not attracted to him but that's where it ends. I don't necessarily want to spend a huge amount of time with him and do feel he's slightly arrogant and can't for the life of me, understand why you still want him to be your best man and call him a friend."

What I didn't want to tell G was that I still went weak at the knees each time I thought of him but that I looked on him as a fantasy, that a lot of women dreamt about but couldn't have.

"Andrew is a friend in the true sense of the word. He has always been there for me when things have gone wrong. He was the first one at my side when he heard I was in hospital after the aeroplane incident, not just to give me moral support but there for me in every sense: ringing people, cancelling appointments, informing work assignments and sometimes even finding replacements for me. When I really need him, he will always be there. So yes, I'm disappointed by his actions but as I said, his heart and mind beat to the rhythm of a different drum."

At this point, I was ready to throw up and the more G praised him, the less I liked him.

On returning from Deal, though I felt a sense of relief, I didn't feel I had suffered enough. I didn't feel I should have got away with what I did, that easily.

Life on a Postcard No. 67
Who Said Romance Was Dead?

I had gone to stay with my parents for the duration of the wedding planning season which, knowing Mother and future Mother-in-law, could take up to a year. The incident with Andrew had somewhat soured and dampened my enthusiasm and excitement for planning the wedding.

Though G had assured me he had forgiven me, I very much doubted I would ever forgive myself. Surely, I needed to be punished for what I'd done? I needed to suffer. G could not be allowed to let me off that easily! Listen to me. Was I even making sense? But that's how I felt. So I started to behave badly. I wouldn't answer his calls, I would say I would meet him somewhere to shop for wedding stuff and then wouldn't turn up. I didn't apologise. I said I was busy all the time. G just accepted all my excuses and put-offs.

Then one night, as I lay sleeping in my old room there was a loud '*tap tap*' on the window which turned into a loud '*bang bang*'. I jumped out of bed, ran to the window and there, outside, was a drone camera which took twenty shots of my shocked face in ten seconds. On the drone was a note: *To my darling wife-to-be, I know what you are trying to do. I have forgiven you. Now you need to forgive yourself. But if you really feel I need to punish you, then I will put these pictures on Facebook. Bissou, G.*

I looked down and smiling up at me through the darkness was G, controlling the drone.

The French were bloody crazy! The romantic gesture, combined with more reassurance from G comforted me, at least for a while.

I had stopped taking Marvin with me most places now, as I felt I needed to bury the ghost and move on with my life. But then, that night I had my last and final dream about Marvin. This time he went to the chemist because he was a *little horse,* as in he had a sore throat but the pun on *'are you a little horse?'* and Marvin insisting he was a moose actually, took up most of the dream.

Life on a Postcard No. 68
Who Needs Freud?

The very next day, there was a huge headline in the newspapers about Forage and Find, the health food chain that Mother, Freya, Gayem and I frequented. Over the last few years, it had grown in size and stature due to the latest craze of foraging. It was well regulated but was dependent on its foragers. Even though they were vetted, clearly one of them had gone astray.

One of its suppliers had started to forage for mushrooms in another part of the country, as his usual haunts had been taken over by councils to build affordable housing. He had, for a few years now, been sending in 'magic mushrooms' that were well known for causing hallucinations! It was only after a health inspection picked this up, that the stories came flooding out.

One lady said, 'Now I understand why I kept thinking I was Maggie Thatcher and would often say to my husband "the lady's not for turning. You turn if you want to, but the lady is not for turning." I never understood why I kept saying that.'

In this article, other people also talked about their experiences. One man was now suing F&F as he had often thought he was a dog and would lift his leg up wherever he was, assuming that was quite normal. He had done this in a meeting and got fired. He then went to see a psychiatrist, who said he couldn't find anything wrong with him and had given him a bone.

'Well thank god!' I said to myself. 'I haven't been having

any such…'

So that's why I'd been having my Marvin the Moose dreams! Freya, Gayem, Mother and I loved mushrooms and we'd bought all our mushrooms from Forage and Find.

The article also said that while the mushrooms would not affect everyone with hallucinations, they were still withdrawing all its mushrooms from all its stores from this particular supplier, who was now under arrest.

I rushed over to my local F&F store and asked them if, by any chance, they had some of the mushrooms left. "No madam, of course not. We've had to withdraw them and even if we did have them, we would not be able to sell them to you."

"What if I danced for you naked? What if I paid you lots of money to watch me dance naked?" I saw the look on their faces and got out of there quickly, before they thought I was still hallucinating from the mushrooms. I needed to find more mushrooms as I knew without them, that was the end of my Marvin dreams.

I suddenly had another thought: Freya, Mum and Gayem!

I rang Gayem first to ask if he had any of the mushrooms left. "Well, thank you for asking whether I'm okay. How are you by the way?"

"I'm fine, Gayem. Did you experience any hallucinations at all? Have you been acting strangely?"

"Not really, Char…" he started to say.

"Well, I guess, how can you tell?" I interjected, sarcastically.

He ignored that and carried on. "I mean, I certainly don't think I'm the Queen. Ha! That's funny, I do know I am *a* queen, but not *the* Queen. Ha! Ha!"

But I had already put the phone down.

I called Mother. Dad picked up the phone.

Me: "Dad, have you heard the news? Has Mum been having any hallucinations that you know of?"

Dad: "Well, it's very difficult to tell with your mother. You see, she often thinks there's a shoe sale on when there isn't and then the other day…"

I disconnected.

Next, I got hold of Freya.

Me: "Have you heard?"

Freya: "Heard what?"

Me: "About F & F. They were selling people magic mushrooms."

Freya: "Oh that. Yes, I had heard."

Me: "Had you been getting any halluci— No, hold on. What's the point of my asking you?"

Freya: "What do you mean? I can have hallucinations just as much as anyone else."

Me: "I know you haven't stopped smoking weed even though you promised us you have, so you're hallucinating all the time."

Freya: "I don't know how you can say that. If I am hallucinating, my hallucinations are just as valid as the next person."

Me: "Well okay then, HAVE you been hallucinating?"

Freya: "How does one tell?"

I gave up.

I would have done anything to get those mushrooms to have my dreams again.

Life on a Postcard No. 69
Wedding Dresses: Surely It Can't Be That Difficult?

And so the wedding preparations began in earnest. The first item on the agenda that Ma and Ma-in-law had was, of course, the wedding dress. I had been prepared for this. I knew they would want to talk about it, so I had done my research. Before they could even finish the phrase 'Wedding Dress', I had whipped out my magazine cuttings and produced the first one to show them.

I said, "I was thinking of something simple, like this one from Marks and Spencer which has got a straight…"

As I was speaking, I could hear deep breathing. I looked up and it was ma-in-law. She had started to hyperventilate.

"Darling, how could you?" Mother said. "She's a dress designer and she's *French*!"

We both tore around the house looking for a paper bag. Not able to find one I grabbed a newspaper and shaped it so that it went over her mouth and nose and told her to take deep breaths. For some unknown reason, she started hyperventilating even more and nearly passed out. All the time she was pointing to the paper.

"Darling, how could you?" Mother said again. "You are trying to help her hyperventilation with *The Daily Mail*! *Quelle domage*!" Mother certainly had been practising her French. As I stood there in complete shock, she raced around and finally found *The Telegraph* to cover her mouth and then ma-in-law finally started to breathe easily.

Once everyone had calmed down, Ma-in-law finally spoke. "C'est un catastrophe! How could you do this to me, Charlotte? You want to buy your wedding dress from Marks and Spencer?" she said, between gritted teeth and then spat a little, just for good measure. "Well maybe your wedding lingerie, maybe some toiletries, but your wedding dress? *Non, Non, Non! C'est impossible!*"

So, I quietly put away all the cuttings I had collected, as I did not want to see what would happen if I showed her the next one from the Littlewoods Catalogue.

Therefore, a fitting with her seamstress was duly booked and we all arrived ready to do battle. Mother and Mother-in-law wanted something elaborate and I was determined to keep it simple.

I was asked to choose a style which would then be made bespoke for me. As we were sifting through the dress samples, Mother-in-law came across one and started shaking and

shuddering. Before she started to spin round on her own axis, I agreed to try it on. It wasn't too elaborate but I wouldn't have chosen it. Of course, it had a corset. How could a French woman choose a wedding dress without a corset?

Once I put it on and came out of the dressing room, all three women — Mother, Ma-in-law and seamstress — tilted their heads to the right at the same time. When I looked at Ma-in-law's face, I knew this was the dress I would have to choose. Tears were streaming down her face and she said, "Oh, Charlotte, you look so beautiful. Would you not *consider* this dress even?"

I said, "No... I will *not* consider it. This *will* be the dress!"

I can safely say that on that day, no French woman was

more pleased that she was. She had been spared the shame of an M&S wedding dress on her daughter-in-law and she got the dress of her dreams.

Then it was time to measure me. I held my chest out, stomach in and squeezed my legs together. "Don't worry," the seamstress said, "you will lose weight by your wedding day." *Really?* I thought. *You don't know me. I will be eating my way to my wedding day.*

Once the measurements were complete, it was time to ask questions to truly make this dress bespoke.

"What colour would Madam like?"

Now I had done some painting in the past, so knew there were many shades of white but was not prepared for the selection of whites in wedding dresses.

I said, "Well, I don't think I should go for pure white, do you?" All three women giggled like teenage schoolgirls who had been told their first naughty joke.

I had to choose from White, Pure White, Off-White, Cream White, Dull White, Bright White, Cream, Jersey White, Jersey Cream, White with a hint of Cream, Cream with a hint of White.

I closed my eyes and pointed to one of them.

"What material would Madam like?"

Before I could close my eyes to point, Hélène said, "We will have organza silk."

"Now, in order to ensure the dress is absolutely perfect for you," said the seamstress, "I will need to ask Madam some personal questions. Is Madam all right with me asking some personal questions?"

"Sure," I said. After all, how personal could it get regarding a dress.

Well, what do you know?

Seamstress: "What kind of a person is Madam?"

Me: "Sorry, what do you mean?"

Seamstress: "I mean, is Madam a happy person, a thoughtful person or a sad person?"

Me: "Sorry, what has that got to do with the dress?"

"Just answer the question, Lottie!" Mother said. "Don't be difficult."

"No, it's quite all right," said the seamstress. "The reason I am asking you, Madam, is that the dress needs to reflect your personality. It needs to be at one with you and your spirit. It needs to flow with you and it cannot do that unless I understand you as a person."

Not being a violent person, I was unsure of what I was feeling at that point and then managed to identify the emotion — rage. I had never wanted to punch someone as much as I did at that moment in time.

But instead, I said, "Well, sometimes I can be very happy, but then there are times when things happen in my life and I become thoughtful and then, the other day, I was walking down the street and all of a sudden huge wave of sadness overcame me."

The seamstress stopped her frantic writing, put her pen down and stared at me, waiting to see if I was joking but I kept a straight face and so she continued.

"What are Madam's favourite things to eat on a full stomach?"

I opened my mouth to object vehemently and looked over at Ma and Ma-in-law, who both shook their heads.

So, I asked, through a saccharine smile, "Could you tell me why this is important, please?"

"Well, Madam, one can tell a lot about one's personality

by what they choose to eat on a full stomach."

I picked the first thing that came into my mind.

"Strawberries," I said.

"How interesting, Madam."

Now I was intrigued. Was she really *not* joking? She was serious about this stuff. Maybe there was something in it. What was I thinking? Of course, there wasn't.

The rest of the questioning was as weird and my answers were as sarcastic.

Does Madam like the hot weather or the cold weather? Hot and cold.

What is Madam's favourite pet? A tarantula.

How does Madam like her tea in the morning? In a mug.

What is Madam's favourite movie? *The Wedding Dress* (Is there such a movie?)

How many times a week does Madam wash her hair? Once a year.

What is Madam's preferred style of communication? With you I would like to communicate through the H Bomb.

And finally…

"Will Madam be consummating the marriage on the wedding night?"

"You can't be serious?" I felt myself slip into McEnroe mode.

Then I realised that out of all the stupid, dumb questions, this was probably the most logical.

My answer was, "After answering all your questions, I will be too tired to consummate anything, let alone on the wedding night."

I begged Ma-in-law to have the fitting for me when the time came and even tried to persuade her we were the same size. She was far slimmer than me.

Life on a Postcard No.70
The Wedding Cake Bake-Off

Exhausted, emotionally, mentally and physically drained from that experience, I stayed away from any more wedding plans for a few days but I was required to be there, when they chose the wedding cake. This time the fathers had been allowed to be there for the tasting but they were not given a vote.

The cake was being made by the brother-in-law of a cousin, who lived next door to the friend of a friend, who had bumped into Harry when he dropped his groceries in front of Waitrose.

Giuseppe was a lovely bustling man with a slightly nervous disposition. He confessed to me that he never feared the bride and groom, only the mothers-in-law. By this time Ma and Ma-in-law had become inseparable. They spoke as 'we' all the time and gave discerning looks in unison, to people who did not agree with their vision of the wedding, or who so much as gave their own opinion. Together they were formidable and I didn't blame Giuseppe for fearing them.

All the various cake pieces with all the different fillings, icings and decorations were laid out on the dining table at G's parents' house. G was there, I was there, the fathers were there and Giuseppe was there. Then the mothers made a grand entrance. They walked straight over to the table and started asking questions.

"Is there one with fruit in?"

"Yes, mesdames."

"Is there one with nuts in?"

"Yes, mesdames."

"Is there a sponge one?"

"Yes, mesdames."

"Is there one with sponge and jam in?"

"No, mesdames, you did not ask for that one."

Giuseppe got the discerning look in unison and I could swear he was about to cry.

They took a bite of each cake like synchronised swimmers, matching the other's gesture.

Finally, they put their forks down. We all waited and I could see Giuseppe literally holding his breath.

It was Ma-in-law who spoke first. "Maybe I should have gone to Maison Blanc."

Giuseppe burst into tears and ran out of the room.

G jumped to his feet "Maman, how could you! How rude! I would like you to apologise to Giuseppe at once!"

Mother now piped up, though she would never have been this bold on her own. However, those two were sucking the evil energy off each other and like pack animals they could smell fear, as well as taste it. And they could taste fear in those cake pieces and they were not going to let go.

"Well, Guillaume, your mother is right. If it is not good enough then he needs to know."

"Who cares what the cake tastes like? Have you ever heard a wedding guest talk about the taste of the cake and say, gosh, that wedding cake wasn't very good, was it? No! They all talk about the *look* of the cake and Giuseppe's cakes look just fine to me. So, who cares?"

"I do," said Mother-in-law. "And I want it to taste and look good at the same time."

Now *I* was feeding off G's energy and getting bolder by the minute. "Well, I like the cakes and after all it is *our* wedding, so we will make the final decision."

Mother said, "You don't understand, Lottie. These decisions cannot be made lightly."

Both fathers thought they had heard enough and it was now their turn to speak.

"Well, we think…" Dad said, but he got no further as he received the discerning look in unison as well. Clearly it had its powers. He stopped dead in his tracks, but Alain nudged him and gave him an encouraging nod.

Egged on by Alain, Father then said, "Now look here, darling and Hélène, I think we have heard enough. The children should decide who makes their cake."

That having been said, an almighty row started between the mothers and fathers. Here they were, supposedly two refined couples and they were arguing about a wedding cake which no one was going to care about or remember.

They raised their voices, waved their arms, pointed and gesticulated and squinted their eyes at each other and then somewhere, somehow, in the midst of it all, Mother-in-law tripped and fell face-first into one of the cake samples.

"How could you?" said Mother to the fathers and picked up another sample cake and threw it at Dad. This prompted Alain to pick one up and throw it at Mum.

Giuseppe re-entered the room, shaking his arms over his head in disbelief while G and I tried to 'extri-cake' the parents from each other.

Suddenly someone shouted, "STOP!" It was ma-in-law. When she had fallen face-first into a cake, she had got a mouth full of it. She was now licking it off her face and said, "This one is very good. Which one is this, Giuseppe?"

"That is the one with the chocolate filling, Madam, but you didn't want that one."

"Well, I like this one. This is the one we will have. Tell me if everyone agrees."

One by one we stood in line with a spoon each, to take some cake off Ma-in-law's face and try some. We all agreed it was the best one.

Life on a Postcard No. 71
Breathing Is an Optional Extra

Soon, it was that time already and I had to go back to try on the wedding dress. I asked Nicole to come with me for some moral support. She arrived with Harry in tow, apologising profusely for bringing him, as all he was going to do was complain that he had to come for the wedding dress fitting, when he could be doing other things in the meantime.

"Why would I complain about that? I don't have my car today so I'm dependent on you, so I have to come," Harry explained

"Well, don't annoy me and keep asking me when we are going to leave because I am telling you now, I don't know when we are going to leave the fitting. We will leave when we are done. I hope that's clear," Nicole replied, as if talking to a child

"But I haven't even asked you anything yet," Harry objected.

"No, you haven't but I know what you're thinking," Nicole carried on in the same vein

"How do you know what I am thinking? Have you become a mind reader all of a sudden?" Harry said, sarcastically.

Nicole delivered the final blow: "I don't have to be a mind reader to read your mind, as there are only a very few pages in there and I know what you are thinking."

I didn't have any popcorn with me at this point as I would

have loved to have sat down and watched, rather than go for the fitting.

They were still arguing when we got there and continued to argue when the seamstress took me into the changing room.

Even though it was only a fitting and not completed yet, I could see what a beautiful dress it was going to be and clearly, she was very talented at what she did and I told her so.

She said, "I could not have done it without truly understanding, Madam."

The least said about that the better, I told myself.

She put the dress on me and then it was time to tighten the corset. Nicole and Harry were still arguing outside, this time about him touching some of the dresses.

"Why do you have to touch them? It's not as if you are going to try them on."

"What's wrong with me touching them? We are in a dress shop, are we not? I have never been in a wedding dress shop before. I can look and touch if I like."

"Well, I just don't see the…"

"Aaaaaaaaaggggghhh!" I screamed from the dressing room. The corset was so tight I couldn't breathe.

After stopping for a split second, Nicole continued. "Right, what was I saying? Oh yes, the dresses…"

I asked the seamstress if she could loosen the corset just a little as I couldn't breathe. She laughed. "No, Madam, of course you can't breathe. Breathing is an optional extra in this dress. Don't worry, you can breathe later."

Somehow, I managed to walk out to my audience on my own steam and for the first time since they left the house, Nicole and Harry were speechless.

From Mother's expression, I knew it had hit the mark. Mother-in-law was sobbing and Sis-in-law ran over to hug me.

Life on a Postcard No. 72
Truffles and Muscles

The wedding arrangements were such: the main wedding would be held in Oxford, where my parents had finally decided to settle. 'Oxford does inspire us so,' they had both said at different times, almost as if to get their stories right.

A marquee would be put up in their back garden and caterers would be brought in. The following week, we would all descend upon the little town of Jambville near Meulin in France, where G originally came from. Both his grandparents were from there and so were his parents. They all now lived in Paris. '*Mais naturellement,*' Mother-in-law would say, 'there is nowhere else one can live. Jambville is lovely, *mais* it is not Paris'.

There would be a reception held in Jambville, where all the French family met in the summer.

Both Alicia and Gayem insisted they wanted to be involved in choosing the wedding menu as they were both foodies and liked to think they had the best taste when it came to grand occasions. At this point, I asked G again if we could elope.

Cousin A and Gayem had met once before at a party Mother had thrown and they had bonded like plane spotters in a by lane. His campness seemed to compliment her snobbery exceptionally well. Who knew the two would go together? She felt he was a great accessory for her and he felt she understood his need for perfection, like no other.

We were meeting at Le Manoir au Quatre Saison in Oxford, as Mother-in-law had given strict instructions to both Alicia and Gayem that she would not tolerate food from anywhere else.

Alicia had rung ahead and asked for the Chef de Cuisine to attend to them personally.

G had conveniently booked a shoot when he heard that Cousin Alicia and Gayem were involved. "*Ma petite pousse*, I can just about cope with each of them individually but together, *c'est impossible*."

As I drove up, I was in awe of the beautiful building looming up ahead of me. I parked up in one of the most beautiful car parks, surrounded by lavender and other herbs. I walked into the restaurant and was really looking forward to the wedding menu tasting, until I saw Cousin Alicia float into the dining area with her nose at the strangest angle, as if there was a steel rod between her nose and the ground which prevented her from lowering her nose as she walked... sorry, *floated*. She reminded me of the receptionist in the Concorde lounge and was very closely followed, by an extremely mincing Gayem.

With a slight wave of her hand, she summoned one of the staff. "We called ahead. We must only speak with the Chef de Cuisine and don't try and pass us off with any old cook." If that didn't ensure we would be getting our taster session spat in, I don't know what would.

I had often told Cousin Alicia she should write a book entitled, *How to win friends and influence people*. Unfortunately, irony and sarcasm were completely lost on Cousin A. They were not concepts she understood, and took me quite seriously whenever I mentioned that topic.

She looked around and saw me sitting in the corner, trying to hide. "Oh, there you are, Charlotte." Having barely acknowledged me, the *actual* bride, she turned to Gayem and said, "Now we absolutely must not be swayed by anything the chef says. He will try and palm us off some second-rate stuff and we have to be razor-sharp when it comes to quality."

Gayem at least started to walk towards me, saying, "Don't you think we need to involve Char in all of these decisions?"

"Don't be silly, she has enough to worry about. We need to take this off her hands," said CA, as if I wasn't there.

I was so tired of all the arrangements, that I decided to go along with that plan for a while.

Soon we were in the presence of the Chef de Cuisine and I didn't think this was possible but *his* nose was on an even longer rigid pole than CA's and being pushed higher by the minute.

It was love at first sight: their eyes met and they were instantly at one with each other. Without exchanging a word, they were able to read each other's minds. CA started to show off her French and they nattered away for a while with a lot of '*mais ouis*' and '*absoluments*'.

Gayem and I stood there smiling at each other awkwardly, wondering whether we should interject but neither of us had the energy.

Soon, Chef went into the kitchens to retrieve something and Alicia turned to us and translated. "I have told Chef that we absolutely cannot have this wedding dinner without truffles. He is going to bring some out to show us."

I had only heard of truffles, (never tried them) and knew that they were ridiculously expensive.

"Really, Cousin A, I don't need truffles at my wedding dinner."

"Nonsense! You cannot possibly have a wedding without truffles," A said.

"And mussels," said Gayem, finally finding his voice.

CA: "I don't think we should have mussels."

Gay: "Why not?"

CA: "Because unless they are absolutely the best quality, they will be awful."

Gay: "Well, I think we should at least ask him."

CA nodded.

"I hate mussels," I said.

"But your guests most probably love them and that's the most important," said CA.

Soon, Chef came back with a large tray on which he had some lumpy bits covered by a damp muslin cloth.

Chef and CA slowly lifted the muslin as if unveiling the *Mona Lisa* they had just stolen.

They both looked at dirty lumps of what looked like clay, CA picked one up and put it to her nose, which was now nearly vertical and took a deep breath.

"*C'est fantastique, non*?" Chef said.

"*Comme ci comme ça. D'ou*?" Cousin A asked.

Chef said, "Tuscany" and Cousin A dropped the lump of clay as if it had just bitten her hand.

"What? You're kidding me? You can't be serious! Everyone knows the best truffles come from Piedmont and you're trying to palm us off with this rubbish?"

"Madam, I do believe the best truffles come from Tuscany and not Piedmont. Who is the Chef de Cuisine here?"

With that ensued, an almighty row. Finally, Cousin A, who was not used to conceding, conceded.

"Okay," she said, "the truffles are not the best but they will have to do."

"Aren't truffles really expensive?" Gayem and I asked, together.

"We don't talk about price when we are planning weddings, Charlotte."

"*You* may not, Cousin A," I said, "but *I* do. What are we going to be paying for them?"

"£3,000 per kilo but that should be enough to feed all your guests," Chef piped up from behind.

All I could see were the wincing faces of Gayem, CA and Chef. What I didn't realise, is that I was screaming at an octave that might have been able to shatter glass.

Whether it was the fact that I was still feeling terribly guilty about my ghastly indiscretion, or whether it was because I was tired, or because everyone else was taking over my wedding, or because I had finally had enough... whatever the reason was, I was not going to tolerate this.

"I don't care what you say, Alicia and I don't care who is paying for this wedding but nothing should cost that much!"

I then launched into a tirade about whether any of them had been to India, how there were people starving in Africa and how some parts of the Far East didn't have running water for days and that amount could possibly be a year's salary of a person in the Third World.

They all listened intently until I had finally finished. It was CA who spoke. She was very calm and responded to me as if I had merely interjected with a mild comment. "How is *not* having truffles at your wedding going to save the world, Charlotte?"

I hate to admit it but she had a point.

However, I think I must have used up the last ounce of energy I had that day and just left her and Gayem to it, got in my car and drove home.

Life on a Postcard No. 73
Which Position Do You Like Best?

It was now time to meet the Vicar. Thankfully, this was something G and I had to do on our own. We could not believe that we were actually going to be taking part in one part of the wedding preparations alone. Peter White had been a friend of the family and Dad's best friend for years and we were so pleased he was able to marry us. Neither of us were very religious, so we were treating this as a formality we had to go through if we wanted a church wedding.

He was a very jolly, fun-loving man who loved life. I remembered having had many invigorating and thought-provoking conversations with him when I was younger.

His wife had sadly died from cancer, his grandson was severely disabled and his daughter now had an aggressive form of breast cancer but it was treatable.

I had once asked him how, with all these illnesses and tragedies, he still believed and had faith. I had, of course, shared with him my loss of faith over Beula. He gave me possibly the best explanation I had heard about God and religion. He said, "God created us in his own image. He then left us to our own devices. He isn't sitting on a throne somewhere saying, "You will live, you will die and you will get a horrible disease". These things happen and they have to be dealt with. When we pray, we don't pray to God to take these nasties away. He can't do that. We pray to him to give us the strength to either change them, or deal with them."

If I was inclined to take up religion, then that was the best version I had ever heard.

But back to the matter at hand. Peter talked to us about companionship and about loving each other and we nodded in unison and made all the right sounds. We found ourselves slowly lulled into a sense of false security.

He then said, "Okay, let's now talk about sex."

We were just nodding off when we both sat upright. Surely he wasn't seriously going to ask us about our sex life? Surely not.

"So, what is your sex life like?" Oh, yes, he was!

"Peter aren't we supposed to wait till after the wedding to have relations?" I said, using the more, what I thought, *appropriate* phrase for what he was about to discuss.

"If I'm wrong about you two having had sex already," — he persisted with that word — "then I will convert to Trekkism."

Not wanting him to give up being a Vicar and become a Trekkie, we mumbled something about having sinned and yes we had indulged in the pleasures of the flesh before wedlock.

"Right, so what is your sex life like?" he said, repeating the question. We both looked at him, lost for words.

He carried on. "Look, you two, sex is a large part of married life. I want to ensure you don't lose sight of that and that you keep that part of it going strong, as well as all the other areas."

He paused to let us take all of that in.

He then said, "So what positions do you use?"

This time G spoke, "Sorry, Vicar, I don't think we heard you right."

"Firstly, Call me Peter. Secondly, you heard me perfectly.

What I am trying to say is don't use the same old boring position each time. Try new things: experiment, explore and don't let your sex life get boring."

At this point, I half-expected Peter to dive into one of his drawers and pull out a flyer for an S&M venue we could visit.

"When Marge was alive, we were very adventurous."

"Woah, Peter," I said. "You are Dad's best friend and I really would rather not hear what you got up to with Aunty Marge."

"All right," said Peter, "but just remember what I've said."

We both left there shell-shocked and looked at each other as if to say, 'Let's not ever talk again of the day we got sex advice from our Vicar'.

Life on a Postcard No. 74
Hollywood Anyone?

No, not the place in L.A. I am talking about the scary, frightening, excruciatingly painful, nightmarish, experience of having your pubic hair completely waxed off. Now you might ask the very valid and very sensible question: Why?

Why in god's name, why in the name of everything holy and why in the name of everything sacred, would *anyone* want to put themselves through the torture? I was posing these questions *after* having been through this blood-curdling experience with a bit in my mouth.

Before I had my hair and possibly half my virginal skin ripped out, I had always thought of having it done but had never been brave enough. The closest I had got to it, was shaving myself each time Freya lost her hair.

However, having had a broken nose and half of my face smashed in, I didn't think there could be any pain worse than that. I was wrong, twice. And this was the first time I was wrong.

I decided to ask Freya what she thought. Bad idea.

"Oh, I've been doing it for years. Look," she said, pulling down her knickers in a flash and revealing some stubble in her nether regions. "Barely any hair there."

"Okay, Okay. I didn't need to see proof, nor did I want a sample or demonstration. Just a simple 'yes I've had it done' would have sufficed."

But as you all know by now, nothing was simple when it

comes to Freya.

I wanted it done now as I wanted to surprise G on our wedding night. So off we went to Freya's lady, "She is abso brill. It will be over before you know it."

First, I had to disrobe completely from the waist down and a towel was discreetly placed over me. Then, the lady walked into the room. She was a large lady and towered above me. She had a hard face that showed no concern or sympathy for someone going through this for the first time. She had a no-nonsense air about her that said, 'I have waxed enough vaginas to fill a duvet and I know what I am doing.'

She first put on some gloves while staring at my vagina, moving her head from side to side like she was looking at a modern-art painting, trying to decide which way was up. She was sizing up her line of attack. She then placed a mask over her mouth and nose.

Fairly insulted, I said, "Thank god my fiancé doesn't do that each time he comes near it." Sensing my discomfort, she said,

"No, madam, this is just for hygiene reasons."

"Yours or mine?" I asked.

She ignored that question and slowly placed her hand on me, while keeping her distance with her body.

She looked like someone who was trying to pick up a cockroach without getting too close to it. She started to paste the wax on, which felt nice and warm. *Well, this isn't too bad*, I thought. What she did next, I wasn't prepared for. Before I even had time to breathe, she ripped the wax off in three quick strokes. The pitch I screamed at, only bitches on heat and Freya could hear.

Even though I could not see the lady's expression

completely as it was obscured by the mask, her eyes were the size of side plates and she pulled the mask off her mouth to admonish me severely. Just then Freya burst into the room and beat her to it. "Do you mind keeping the screams down! There is a group of ladies out there all waiting to go in and now you've scared the shit out of them. One has already left the salon!"

"Well, forgive me for expressing my extreme agony," I said, "but it's bloody, f%*&ing painful."

"It's not *that* bad," Freya said.

The waxing lady, who now began to resemble Attila the Hun, turned her attention to Freya and said, "I can handle this, Madam. Please leave the room."

Freya was not used to being told what to do, but knowing she was next, she complied.

Attila then proceeded to work around the area like a skilled gardener with some very powerful, dangerous and painful sheers. She did this without expression and completely ignoring my screams and yells and 'That was bloody painful' comments.

Finally, it was over, Or not.

Attila: "Can you now turn over, Madam?"

Me: "What for?"

Attila: "For the back, Madam."

Me: "Back? I don't need anything done at the back."

Attila: "Between the crack, Madam. It has to be removed."

Me: "No, no, it really doesn't. Nothing needs to be removed from the back."

Attila: "It will not have a neat finish."

Me: "I think we can dispense with a neat finish this time.

I really don't mind."

Attila: "I have to finish it, Madam."

I wanted to say, 'Why? You're not exactly Van Gogh, where years from now someone might say, "Shame he didn't paint a smile on that woman". You're not exactly Vermeer and centuries later someone might say, "Wouldn't this painting have really looked better if that girl had had a pearl earring?'

Instead, I just turned around and obeyed.

She then literally poured wax into the crack and yanked it off with such vigour I thought my tonsils would be sucked out through my bottom.

I couldn't get off the bed soon enough and charged out of there. As I ran, I began to realise that actually I was able to run faster! I had no friction and was able to fly at Freya faster than I would have done before. I lunged at her and screamed, "I would rather have had my nose broken again!"

For my wedding, I had something new (my dress), something borrowed (Mother's pearls) and now I had something blue (my hairless, bruised vagina).

Apart from it being blue, I must say I was whizzing about everywhere and it did feel much better but I kept remembering the pain and I gave up the idea of ever having it done again.

Life on a Postcard No. 75
D-Day

Correct me if I am wrong but the day of your wedding is supposed to be one of pampering and indulging. I got nothing of the sort. I was woken up at 6 a.m. by Cousin Alicia and Gaymen screaming at me down the phone, arguing with each other about something.

One of them and it really wasn't important which one, had mixed up all the table settings and I was needed urgently to help with the place names. I was staying at a hotel overnight so that I could 'rise calmly', get dressed 'at leisure' and be ready for my big day.

Clearly, none of that was going to be allowed to happen. I arrived at Chez Nous at the point Alicia was ready to kill Gaymen, who was screaming like a banshee and running around the tables. I managed to calm both of them down and we started to sort out the names and places.

We were just about finished, when I heard a blood-curdling shriek from Cousin A. Standing in the background was G. He had popped in to pick up his morning suit that had arrived at the house. With all the professionalism, precision and speed of presidential security men whisking the United States President off to safety when there is a threat, Alicia and Gaymen whisked me out of the gazebo, through the conservatory and out of the front door, unceremoniously slamming the door in my face!

"You cannot see each other on your wedding day, it's *such*

bad luck!" came the muffled voice of Cousin A from behind the front door.

I started to shout, "But my handbag is still…" at which point, it was thrown out at me and the door slammed in my face again.

"I don't see why I have to leave if he's come to pick up his suit," I shouted again but it was no use. I could hear her screaming at G for being so thoughtless and inconsiderate.

"But how was I supposed to know she would be here?" I could hear G's voice, trailing in the distance.

Finally, a calming presence arrived in the form of Freya. Alicia was a little bit scared of her but refused to admit it. Gayem was *very* scared of her and had no problem admitting it.

"You," she said, pointing at Alicia, "stop being so ridiculous. Do you really think him seeing her today is going to be bad luck? I never saw a black cat or walked under a ladder but ended up with one less breast. How the bloody hell do you think that happened?"

Freya had started to play the cancer card with gay abandon and was loving it. It was like she had suddenly discovered there was a whole world out there that she could benefit from, due to the fact she'd had cancer:

• Starbucks: Would you mind if I just get through the line, please? Breast cancer you know.

• Tube: Would you mind if I sit down. Just finished chemo treatment, (Yeah, months ago!)

• Nightclubs: You aren't going to charge a woman with breast cancer, are you?

• Cinema: I heard you gave a special discount to breast cancer victims?

• Mortgage company: I believe if you have breast cancer you are allowed a mortgage holiday. Is that true? Cough, cough. Excuse me. Sorry, it's one of the side effects.

Anyway, where was I? Oh yes, getting married.

I was fairly calm when Father came to pick me up from the hotel. There was a knock on the door, I opened it and saw him standing there in his top hat and tails and two things happened: 1. I looked at Father and thought, I have never seen him look so handsome in my life, 2. it was at this point I started to feel butterflies which turned into small birds, which then turned into galloping gazelles. He told me I had never looked so beautiful and I took one last look at myself in the mirror.

The dress had had to be taken in yet again, as the seamstress — though I hate to admit it —had been right and I had lost weight before the wedding. The dress clung to me and my body was swathed and wrapped in endless yards of some shade of cream, silk organza. I can't even remember which one I'd pointed to now. My veil was full-length and I slowly covered my face with the front of it, took a deep breath, grabbed Dad's arm and left the hotel.

Cousin A's husband, Tris the wank... sorry banker, had insisted on taking me to the church in his pride and joy, which was an open-topped, 1945, Rolls Royce. It was a beautiful car and so I'd agreed.

As we drove down the streets of Oxford, past Christ Church College, past the Thames, past the Ashmolean Museum, people waved, shouted congratulations and also hollered, 'Don't do it! Don't do it!' I also got another piece of advice from a youth about to jump into the Thames as they sometimes did in summer: 'You'll get less for murder, darling'.

We got to the church and now my heart was really pounding, so much I thought it would jump out of my chest and run down the aisle in front of me, as if on speed.

Peter came out to meet us. "Are you ready?" he asked, rhetorically.

"As I will ever be," I said.

"It's never too late to back out, you know," he said, with a wink.

We started to walk slowly down the aisle behind him, followed by Freya, Nicole and CA; the last two having both insisted on being my bridesmaids. But I also had Gayem as one of my bridesmaids and they all looked beautiful in their synchronised dresses and suit.

This day was as close to perfection as it could get.

As I walked down the aisle, I could see friends and family smiling at me. I waved to them as I passed them by. I could see the General and Mrs Modi, who I blew a kiss to. It was lovely of them to have made the trip all the way from Hyderabad. I saw Mr Raju and his family, who I winked at as I brushed past them. Then I saw G, looking decidedly nervous and twitchy and next to him, was Andrew looking more handsome, than I had ever seen him before.

Andrew was looking a bit uncomfortable in tails as he very rarely wore clothes, let alone a suit but it still made my heart sprout little wings and take a flight around my chest, before it eventually settled back down again. Why did he still make me feel this way? Bizarrely, the questions — Did I make the right decision and could it have possibly worked with Andrew? — crossed my mind. I shook the feeling off as quickly as it came over me. How could I possibly think like that? What was wrong with me? It was just nerves, I reassured myself.

Dad and I finally came to rest next to G. Just as Father was about to hand me over to him, I stopped, turned on my heel and ran back down the aisle again. There was a collective sharp intake of breath from the guests and Gayem shrieked and started to fan his face with his hand. I kept running till I was face to face with Zaheer's parents. I had felt the urge to give them a big hug and tell them how much it meant to me to have them there. They were visibly touched and so was I.

There was another sharp sigh of relief from the guests as they realised, I wasn't about to leave G at the altar.

I walked briskly back, grabbed G's arm and told him to stop being so nervous. As I did so, I realised there was no other decision; the other one had been a fantasy that not just I but *no one* could live out. In fact, I came to the conclusion that even Andrew was living in his own fantasy and that while some were lucky enough to live their fantasy for a while, at some time they had to start living in the real world. I needed the real world more than the fantasy: the fantasy had taken me on a journey, helped me to fly and feel like I could do virtually anything. That was how he made me feel when I was with him but the real world made me feel safe. I wasn't giving one up for the other. I was *choosing* the man who loved me truly, madly, deeply, rather than the man who wanted to swing me around, take me to great heights… and then what?

Both G and I turned to face Peter and we looked at each other, with visions of the missionary position looming in front of us.

It was hard to keep a straight face after that throughout the service but somehow, we managed it.

Gayem had convinced us that, as he was one of the

bridesmaids, that we should let his poodle be the ring-bearer. He had been training her for weeks. So, at the appropriate time when Peter turned to him and said, "Do you have the rings?" Gayem whistled and Ms Truly Scrumptious came running down the aisle. It was all going smoothly and according to plan, as she was supposed to run down the aisle, jump into Gayem's arms and Peter would take the rings off her collar. Instead, she ran straight into Peter's arms and started licking him all over. Everyone burst out laughing, while a rainbow-faced Gayem tried to get her off Peter. He failed miserably till Aunt Sybil, who was laughing loudly, started chortling, coughing and then snorting. This distracted Truly, who stopped licking Peter, fell from his arms and ran over to Aunt Sybil and started to snarl at her. Sybil then started shrieking and this annoyed Truly even more and she started to nip at her feet, which made Sybil hop and shriek some more.

All this time, Gayem was shrieking as well and falling over all the guests to try and get to Sybil and Truly. Finally, he managed to grab hold of her — Truly, I mean, not Aunt Sybil — though someone should have grabbed hold of her as well, as she was about to faint and he brought Ms TS back to rest in her appointed position, with the rings.

Finally, calm was restored. Peter took the rings off Truly, who was still trying to lick him and we carried on with the ceremony, while Gayem kept mumbling and scolding Truly, telling her she would not be getting any treats for a week.

As I had been barely involved in the organisation of this wedding, I was pleasantly surprised to find that Freya had organised 'My love is like a Red Red Rose' to be sung by a one-legged singer, who sang it beautifully. That was another side effect of her cancer: she was now partial to anyone who had lost one of anything. She had driven CA mad, much to my delight, trying to find a one-armed, one-legged or one-breasted florist. They had finally found one who was wheelchair-bound, who had lost both her legs in an accident. Freya was delighted. This went way beyond her expectations. She also managed to convince both mothers to go with a wedding organiser who had lost three fingers in a 'releasing doves' accident. (Please don't ask.)

She wasn't very happy with the choice of Giuseppe, who made the wedding, cake as he was completely able-bodied but she comforted herself that as he was Italian, he was disabled enough already.

Life on a Postcard No. 76
A Speech in Time

It was time for the father of the bride to give his speech.

During the lead up to the wedding, both Mother and I had been asking Father quite subtly what he was going to say in his speech.

"I have it all in hand, darlings, don't you worry." And so we worried; we worried a lot. Then, closer to the wedding we asked him not so subtly whether he had prepared his speech and what he was going to say.

"Now, now, darlings," Father patted me on the leg, reassuringly, "I have delivered speeches to both Houses of Parliament, I have stood up and addressed both The House or Representatives and the Senate, I have spoken extempore at Buckingham Palace during a gala dinner, so giving a speech at your wedding is not going to be difficult. Please don't give it another thought."

Mother and I gave it lots of thoughts: we lay awake thinking about it, we thought about it in the shower, we thought about it while having breakfast and then finally, it was Mother who came out and said it.

"Now, darling, you won't embarrass us, will you? It's your only daughter's wedding and we have been planning for this. Every last detail has been taken into account, so please practise your speech and make sure you know what you are going to say."

Dad let rip. "Now look here, you two. Do you really think

I am going to embarrass my daughter at her own wedding? My pride and joy, the little bundle that at three days old grabbed my little finger and held onto it so tightly and has been twisting me around it ever since? Do you think I would embarrass her?"

Now it was time. Both Mum and I sat holding our breath... well, I had been holding mine ever since the seamstress had sewn me into my wedding dress that morning, so I should say I *kept* holding mine.

Father got up to speak. He looked around the room and smiled. Mother and I looked at each other and started to relax a little. Perhaps he had written something down, perhaps he had prepared...

No. We couldn't see a paper. There was no hand going into his pocket to take out his notes.

We looked back at each other and saw panic in each other's faces.

Father had stopped smiling. He cleared his throat.

He had dried up. He didn't know what to say. Yes, he might have addressed both Houses of Parliament but this was his daughter's wedding and he was not having to give a speech on political science, economics or world affairs. This was his little girl, his little bundle, who only a few short years earlier had held his hand, looked into his eyes and said, 'I love you, Daddy. You are the best Daddy in the world'. His little cherub, who would squeal and squeal when he grabbed hold of her and tickled her. His little angel, with whom he'd had to gather into his arms and rush up the hospital steps so she wouldn't die. His little brave thing, who only very recently had fallen into his arms, clung onto him and sobbed uncontrollably when her heart was breaking. His little princess, who today was in a wedding dress and was about to become someone else's. She wouldn't be his little nightingale anymore — she would be someone's wife.

This was *very* different from giving a speech in the Houses of Parliament.

He cleared his throat again.

"Ladies and gentlemen, today my daughter is getting married. It's a miracle!" The audience laughed. *Okay*, Mum and I thought, *perhaps it won't be so bad after all.*

Wrong!

"I will tell you why it is a miracle, because her whole birth was a miracle."

No! Both Mum and I tried to gesture to Father, who was now in full swing and had finally found his stride, like a runaway train finds its momentum heading downhill towards a great, Big Crash!

"My wife was pregnant and the doctors told her she wouldn't have this baby as she had fibroids the size of footballs in her uterus." So, not only was he giving the miracle-birth speech *again*, he was now using gynaecological terms to describe it!

Both Mum and I had our faces in our hands and were shaking our heads.

"Don't be embarrassed, darlings," Dad said. "There is nothing to be embarrassed about."

We looked at the audience, who were by now just about composing themselves and getting ready for the next episode of *Casualty*, that Father was now building up towards.

He went on to tell the bewildered and shocked audience, how finally and *miraculously* the fibroids moved out of the way and how none of the doctors could believe it and therefore all the trainee doctors were called in to give Mother an internal examination.

And finally, Father turned to me and said, "So, that is the story of my miracle baby and darling, I just hope you don't have fibroids in *your* uterus."

It will come as no surprise to you to know, that there was very little uptake of the next course. CA was devastated when there were dozens of lavender and vanilla mousses served with strawberries and a blueberry coulis left over.

Father has never been allowed to speak in public since.

Life on a Postcard No. 77
Oooo la la! The Wedding Night! Or Should I Say Morning!

I'm sure you are all wondering whether the dress had been designed to consummate the marriage that night. But by the time we got to our hotel it was 4 a.m. We decided we were too tired to even take our clothes off, to change into our pyjamas. We flopped on the bed, turned out the light and were just about to drift off into La La Land when the bed started to move and sway. We both jumped up with me saying, "Okay, I know sex with you is good, but it's not *that* good to make the earth move, even when you're not touching me!"

Before we knew it, Andrew, Cousin A, Gayem, Freya and three of our other friends had pounced out from under the bed with bottles of champagne and bunches of roses! How they all got under the bed in the first place I will never know. Just as well as I asked, because this is how they did it.

Apparently, they all first lay down and asked the room attendants to place the bed on top of them!

We then had another hour of raucous revelry and by the time we got to sleep it was 6 a.m. This time I *did* take off the dress and we *did not* consummate the marriage that day.

Life on a Postcard No. 78
Couldn't They Have Chosen A Better Word For 'Honeymoon'?

What do you mean? Like what? Like:

'OMG! Is this who I've married?'

'Is it too late to get it annulled?'

'I have to live with *this* for the rest of my life?'

'How could I have not seen this before?'

'I have lived with you for a year and I didn't know *any* of this.'

'Help!'

'I want my Mum!'

We did the traditional thing of going away on our honeymoon, the day after the wedding and we chose Morocco. It was one of the few places G and I hadn't been to and really wanted to visit.

One thing I learnt about marriage is that the 'honeymoon period' does not even last as long as the honeymoon!

G had done all the organising as he was the travel photographer, so surely knew what he was doing. Wrong again!

We got off the plane in Marrakesh, where I was expecting a suited and capped chauffer standing there with a lovely plaque with the names 'Mr and Mrs Laurent' on it. That was quite exciting as it would be one of the first times I would see my married name on paper.

So, I was expecting chauffer, white cap, suited… but we descended into a crowded terminal and had to fight our way through the crowds to finally be pushed out onto the pavement to wait for a taxi.

Disappointing!

Then I corrected myself. I was beginning to think like Cousin A. Perhaps I had spent too much time with her during the wedding preparations. However, I just thought that on our honeymoon it would be nice not to 'rough it', as G always wanted to.

We finally managed to get a taxi and G gave him the name of the place we were staying. We started to drive and we drove past the five-star hotels with their swimming pools, mini bars, turn-down service, mints on the pillows and their twenty-four-hour room service.

I looked at G who seemed very excited about where we were going. We then drove past the four-star hotels with their piped music in the lifts, all-you-can-eat breakfast buffets and luxury beds. Still, we did not stop.

We then drove past the three-star hotels with their plastic glasses by the bed side, powdered milk and granules you could loosely call 'coffee' on a nightstand and clean sheets on the bed.

I looked at G. Surely, we were going to stop there? But no, we carried on. Then, the wide, clean streets started to disappear. They started to get narrower and dirtier. Finally, we came to a stop in front of an arch.

"Car cannot go further," the taxi driver informed us. By now, G was shaking he was so excited. I got out of the taxi only to be faced with a man dropping his trousers and pooing right in front of me by the roadside.

I looked at G and he gave me a reassuring smile.

"'Isn't it just like India? I think you will feel right at home here."

Those weren't my exact thoughts. My thoughts were, *If I'd wanted to feel like we were in India I would have asked to go to bloody India!* But I kept the faith and waited to see what was next in store. I would reserve judgement.

We then had to lug our suitcases at least two hundred yards and came to stop outside a large, wooden door. G banged the knocker and within seconds, it was opened by a dark-haired, olive-skinned man who had clearly left the sun bed on too long and was now looking a deep shade of satsuma orange.

"Welcome to my riad," he said. We walked in and I could now see the reason for G's excitement. The riad was an old traditional house with authentic Moroccan furniture, tiles and decor. It was a heaven among the muck! I really could not believe such gems existed in areas such as this. The whole riad was laid out on different levels with a fountain in the middle of the house. If you stood by it and looked up, you could see through a remarkably large skylight. Our room, with a dressing room, was to die for. Just as well I had kept my mouth shut.

Marrakesh was really the best choice. We needed to relax and that is what we did. Even the call to prayer which woke us each morning at 5 o'clock was so beautiful and melodic, that we would wake up, turn over and go back to sleep again. We had tea and breakfast on our balcony every morning, stayed in the shade till the evening and then wandered around the streets and markets drinking copious amounts of freshly squeezed orange juice.

The market places were buzzing and we brought home many souvenirs. We realised that for one of the few times in our lives, we were actually tourists and we made full use of that status, doing all the things tourists would traditionally do.

Life on a Postcard No. 79
A Reception in Paris? How Very Chic!

It was time to leave for Paris, for the French reception. The plans had been underway for a while and Ma-in-law got shriller and more hyper as the time got closer. Her darling son was getting married and she wanted it all to be perfect. I think in her own mind she didn't consider the wedding in UK to be a real 'wedding' and even though we had just returned from our honeymoon, she still kept talking about 'when you get married in Paris'.

"You are spending more time planning this wedding and taking more care over this wedding than you did for mine," Nicole said to her during one of our 'Paris wedding' meetings. Hélène had folders for everything. The 'Englich' — wedding folder had been put away but brought back out again on several occasions, to double-check points and take the best bits of that for this.

"Come on now, darling," Ma-in-law reprimanded her, "your wedding was planned by your mother-in-law, who did not want me to interfere as you had only one wedding in Italy and only wanted a low-key affair. You chose to take the money instead! What could I do?"

"You have always favoured Guillaume over me!" said Nicole and stormed out of the room.

"Zat is so like her," said Hélène and carried on doing what she was doing.

"I think I should go and see what's upsetting her," I said.

"Oh, she will come back. Zat girl is always upset about something. I cannot keep up."

I was just about to go and see to her when she returned, apologised and carried on with the plans. Later, I asked her what the problem was and why the outburst. She explained she had been having more problems with Harry: not only was he stubborn but he didn't listen and now the football season had started, he barely paid her any attention and she was feeling neglected.

Nicole and Harry were a great match. They fought hard, loved hard, played hard. We all knew that and they knew that. So, like all the other times, I just patted her on the back and said it would work out.

"Not this time," she said. "This time it's different. I have explained to Harry that as we have no children, we have to work harder at our marriage as we don't have that glue sticking us together." She was right about that.

Years earlier, when they had first met, they had been attracted to each other not only for the usual reasons but also because neither of them wanted children. That was something they were both resolute about from the start. Their lives were their own and they fought off all pressure from both parents, in order to live their lives the way they wanted to and I had always admired them for that.

So in this instance she was right: not having children could work both ways.

I then took her a little bit more seriously and asked whether every football season was the same and she confirmed that it was. "So, what's different this time?" I asked.

"I'm not sure. I think he is taking me for granted. I think he feels that every football season I should accept that I won't have a husband for a while and I'm not happy with that."

"Nicole, I am going to give you that same advice I give you each time you come to me with something like this: talk to him about it."

"I have but it really hasn't helped."

"Then talk to him again," I said.

"Okay, I will try," said Nicole and we left it at that

Plans for Paris carried on in full swing.

Hélène, Alain, G, myself, Nicole and Harry were going to go on ahead and my parents, Freya, Adrian and Gayem were going to come later.

"You have done enough, Vera," Hélène said to Mother. "Now it's my turn. I want you to just relax."

Both G and I had tried initially to deter Hélène from having a Parisian reception, as all the French family and friends had managed to make it for the English one. But she wouldn't hear of it.

"Such a colossal waste of money," G kept telling his mother.

"You are my only son and, hopefully, this is a once-in-a-lifetime thing so let me indulge myself."

The day of the flight was upon us and Nicole called. "I can't take it anymore!" she shouted down the phone.

I had heard this so many times before, that I dismissed it with the usual, "Nicole, stop being dramatic, we can work this out. I'm in a rush; I can't deal with this now. Let's talk about it at the airport." She reluctantly agreed, realising it was a bad time.

When we met at the airport, all through check-in, both Nicole and Harry were uncharacteristically quiet. Usually, when they had rows they screamed and shouted at each other, no matter who was listening or where they were.

Once we checked in, I took Nicole aside and asked her to talk me through this most recent issue.

"He won't listen," she said. "I have tried to talk to him and he won't listen."

Me: "Have you really tried to explain to him in a calm manner how you feel, or have you yelled it at him?"

Nicole: (quite truthfully) "I have done both. I have even cried, which as you know, I never do."

Me: "Okay, do you need G or me to intervene?" (We had done this once before when they were both being so stubborn, we had to talk to them in order to plan the wedding outfits or they wouldn't have got done on time. We don't like to intervene but if needs must...)

Nicole: "I don't think it will do any good this time."

Me: "Well, let us at least try."

Nicole was about to reply when the others called us to board.

I started walking towards them. Harry was still looking glum but the expression on his face said, "I know you are going to say something to me and I am prepared."

I had nearly reached the others when I realised Nicole was not by my side. I looked back and she was still rooted to the same spot.

"Come on, Nicole," I said.

"No," she said, "you carry on. I can't get on that plane. I'm telling you, my marriage is over."

Now Hélène was getting impatient. "Nicole, you really do pick the wrong moments to be dramatic. Don't ruin your brother's wedding like this. Let's talk about it later."

"No, you don't understand!" Nicole shouted.

"Well, help us understand when we get there," I said.

By this time, the ground staff were pushing for us to get on as they were about to close the doors.

We were all getting a little bit edgy now and Hélène and I screamed at her in unison. "Come on, Nicole. We're going to miss our plane!"

She shouted back, "You don't understand — I want a baby now and he doesn't!"

All of us, including the ground staff, stopped in our tracks.

They needed to close the aircraft doors. I told the others to carry on and I would stay with Nicole and bring her on a later flight. They had no time to argue as the ground staff ushered them onto the plane. They strained their necks to look back at us, each one with a terribly worried expression, except Harry, who looked straight ahead.

G mouthed 'Will you be okay?' to me. I nodded and they were gone.

I turned to Nicole, gave her a big hug and led her slowly to a seat. She was now sobbing and the very kind ground staff who had heard the whole drama unfold, brought her a glass of water and a cup of tea.

Why is it in England we think everything can be solved with a 'nice cuppa tea'? But surprisingly, the bloody thing does work. There is nothing that happens to us in this world that a nice cuppa cannot make better.

I remember when I was cabin crew, I was helping to board one particular flight when a little old lady got on in Barbados. She was sobbing. Gayem was at the door with me and she started sobbing on his shoulder and when he asked what was wrong, she said, "My husband is in the hold. He had a heart attack when we were on holiday and dropped dead when paragliding. So, we ordered a casket to take him back and he's now in the cargo hold."

"Oh dear, I'm so sorry to hear that," Gayem said. He then paused for a few seconds, put on his best sympathetic face, put his arm around her shoulder and said, "Never mind. Come and have a nice cup of tea." And none of us, including the lady, thought there was anything wrong with that

Back to Nicole. I gave her time to sob and then asked her slowly, "So it wasn't about him?" She shook her head. "And it wasn't about football season?" She shook her head again. "When did you start to feel this way?"

"A few months ago. I was walking through the park on the way back from work."

Nicole being a jewellery designer worked for an exclusive jeweller in London; so exclusive that none of us really knew where they were located. Apparently, they made jewellery for the Queen but that rumour had never been confirmed. Hélène was most impressed about this, as was she a huge royalist.

Nicole walked through Hyde Park each day on her way to work. On this particular day, she was deep in thought about a particular design of necklace she was developing.

Then, in the distance she heard, "Mama! Mama!" She turned around and said, "'Ye—'" then stopped, realising what she was about to say. That preoccupied the whole day and when she got home that evening, she told Harry, who laughed it off and said it was probably because she had been deep in thought and didn't realise even where she was.

Nicole saw it differently. She saw it as a Freudian slip. Not that Nicole knew anything about Freud and his theories but she did know what she felt and what she felt was too strong to ignore.

She realised at that moment that she had changed and she now wanted what she never thought she would want. With Nicole, who was so single-minded, so determined and so independent, this would not have been something that someone could suggest to her or if she saw a friend having a baby, she might get broody over. This was something she would have felt very strongly herself, with no inference from anyone else.

Harry apparently brushed it off each time she broached the subject, as a 'phase' she was going through.

Nicole said she had tried to talk to him many times over the past few months, but there was no point. He accused her of 'breaking their agreement'.

"I never knew we had one, Charlotte. He's behaving like I signed a pre-nup on not having a child."

"He's accused me of going back on my word and when I told him I didn't think the marriage could endure if he felt differently, he said I wasn't being fair to him and that just because that I felt this way now, didn't mean he had to as well. And he's right. He can't just change his mind because I feel differently. But at the same time, I don't think I can stay with someone who has such fundamental opinions that differ from the way I want to live the rest of my life and I now feel I want to have a child."

"Do you want a child more than you want Harry?" I asked. That was a tough question and I admired the way she answered it.

"No, I want a child *with* Harry, but if he doesn't want one, I can't stay with him, as I will resent him for it."

This was going to be challenging. I could see both sides.

By this time, the ground staff had rebooked us on the next flight which was due out in half an hour.

I turned to Nicole. "What do you want to do?" I said. "I would love to miss my own wedding reception in Paris and elope with you to somewhere else but I don't think your brother and mother would forgive me: your brother because he would have to face your mother's wrath all on his own and your mother because two hundred and fifty mini macaroons and petits fours that she has organised, along with everything else, will go waste!"

"Charlotte, you can always make me laugh even at the worst of times," Nicole said and with that, we boarded the next flight to Paris and didn't talk of babies or anything remotely serious. Instead, we got completely pissed on a combination of red wine, white wine and champagne and I'm sure we managed to down a vodka chaser — all in fifty minutes!

We talked about the wedding and how '*Maman*' as she now insisted on being called, had driven us all mad with the macaroon fetish. If the English wedding couldn't happen without truffles, then the French wedding could not happen without macaroons and most certainly could not happen without parsley. Mother-in-law made it very clear to the caterers that parsley had to be the 'garnish *du jour*' or heads would roll. I do believe they pre-ordered the parsley from the market in case they ran out, as Hélène put the fear of the herb god into them. So, we drank ourselves silly and laughed about anything and everything.

We arrived at the hotel. I had texted G to ensure he stayed in the same room as Harry, as Nicole and I would be sharing a room that night.

G had already had a long conversation with Harry on the

flight and briefed me on it when we arrived. Harry felt that Nicole was going back on a decision they had both made before getting married. She had been absolutely resolute in her mind that she did not want children and now, a few years into the marriage, she had changed her mind.

G, who was always very good at these sorts of discussions, agreed with Harry and said he could see it from his point of view but that he must accept, that Nicole had a right to change her mind as well.

Nicole wanted to leave all negotiations and discussions about this till after the wedding but I wanted to make it very clear to Harry, that it didn't look to me like Nicole was going to change her mind. I met him briefly after we had settled into our room and Nicole was in the shower, to explain to him that she was now resolute in the fact she wanted a child and speaking from a woman's perspective, that was not about to change any time soon. So, if this was something he could not and would not consider, then he must be prepared to lose her.

"Oh, and she loves me so little that she is happy to lose me over this?"

"Well, clearly she is not," I said, "and that is why she has tried to talk to you so many times about it but you won't even talk to her and keep brushing it off as a *phase*. It's clearly not a phase, so the choice is now yours."

I left the conversation at that and Nicole and I decided to get some R&R and do some sightseeing before the big Macaroon Fest.

Throughout the day, I kept getting texts from G, asking where we were and what we were doing. Bless him. He was probably missing me and concerned that I was having to babysit his sister.

I then got a call from G asking me whether we had reached the Eiffel Tower and got another call from him halfway up, to find out whether we had reached the top. When we were right at the top of the tower, I got another call from G.

By now, I was beginning to get very annoyed and was about to tell him to stop calling me when he said, "Keep her up there as long as you can."

"What?" I was about to say when I saw Nicole's face change to a look I had never seen before: a combination of shock, disbelief and joy.

I followed her gaze way up into the sky. She was looking directly at a light aircraft, circling round the Eiffel Tower over and over again. Attached to the rear of this aircraft was a long banner which read: NICOLE, I LOVE YOU. LET'S MAKE A BABY.

I walked over to her, put my arm around her and squeezed her shoulder. She grabbed the hand that was on her shoulder and squeezed it even tighter. Then she looked at me and burst into tears. I called G: "Operation Sucking up has been a success," I said. "You guys did very well."

G said, "Hallelujah! The macaroons are saved!"

Life on a Postcard No. 80
The Massive Macaroon Marriage

Ma-in-law insisted on having one hundred people at the Ritz. She had designed yet another dress for me and this time, due to the blue lips and shortness of breath at my English wedding, she decided there would not be a basque with this one and she would give me room to breathe normally. But this time I had to survive the indignity of a 'fascinator'.

"It really does give it that *chic-ness*, Charlotte," she said, each time I tried to avoid wearing it. Finally, I gave in and donned this feathery contraption on my head, barely above my right eye.

During the reception, I noticed Nicole and Harry were the calmest and closest I had ever seen them. It wasn't normal and each time Harry did something silly, like trip over someone or something, I saw Nicole about to say something and then stop herself.

Finally, when I saw Harry looking one way, while chatting to someone and pouring himself a glass of champagne, which then fell over a baby's head nearly drowning it as it crawled on the floor, I had to say something, as Nicole was biting her tongue.

I rushed over to him and said, "For goodness sake, Harry. Can't you see what you're doing? Why can't you just concentrate on one thing at one time? Do you realise how frustrating it is being your sister-in-law and how embarrassing it is?"

There was a very long, twenty-second silence from both Harry and Nicole who stood there staring at me, stunned. I enjoyed that twenty seconds as that was the last time, they would be quiet. Harry then mouthed the words 'Thank you' to me, and Nicole said, "'I'm so glad someone said something as I was about to burst!"

Harry picked up the baton. "Nicole, my angel, just because we have decided to have a baby doesn't mean we have to change how we are with each other. It was killing me that you were not yourself around me and I don't think we would survive being a normal couple."

Finally, the silence had been broken and the rest of the evening resumed as normal, with them having a go at each other.

As Father had been forbidden from speaking in public, we decided that Alain should be the only one to do a speech at the French reception and it would be a far more sensible and normal speech — it would be eloquent and lovely.

After the main course and just as the long-awaited macaroons were being served and placed in front of us, Alain clinked his champagne glass gently with his knife, cleared his throat and took out his papers on which he had written his notes and he put on his glasses. You could see all the guests visibly settle down in their seats, ready for the speech. I looked across at Dad as if to say, 'You see? *This* is how you prepare for and deliver a speech'.

Alain started and spoke, of course, in French. He said, "When Hélène and I got married, we decided we wanted four children. Unfortunately, that was not to be. When we acquired Harry, our dream was nearly complete and now that Charlotte has joined our family, we now have the four children we wanted."

There was a collective 'Awwwwww' from the French audience. I looked across at Father again as if to say, 'Now *this* is how you give a wedding speech'.

Alain continued in French. "Now I could give you a lot of detail of when Guillaume was young, how he and Charlotte met and how lovely they are together and maybe I will come to that in a few minutes but first I *must* translate for those of you who were not at the English wedding, the most fascinating speech the father of the bride gave a few weeks ago. 'Charlotte was a miracle baby...'"

I buried my face firmly into my plate full of mini macaroons.

Life on a Postcard No. 81
Ah, Married Life

During the first year of our marriage, we... Blah Blah Blah. You know how it goes for the first year of marriage. We settled into married life and all the stuff that went with it: we fought about the decor, we fought about the pictures on the walls and we fought about bedding. G won every time because he was French. Apparently, it's an unwritten rule and in fact I think it's even a written rule, that if you are French you have better taste than anyone else.

Nicole, having secured commitment from Harry that he was open to trying for a baby, then decided she wanted to wait a bit before trying, as she said she had a huge jewellery contract to finish. "Typical Nicole," Harry said.

We had the obligatory *family* Sunday lunches together — when I say *together*, I mean both sets of parents, Nicole, Harry and us — which usually turned out be a mixture of fun, frolic and arguments but only a few families might relate when I ask, how can an argument start when all parties are in total agreement?

One particular Sunday, we started to talk about fox hunting and all was going well. There were nods and 'I agree' and 'You are absolutely right' flying all over the place and everyone was in agreement, that whichever way you looked at it, fox hunting needed to be banned and how it could be called a sport was beyond anyone at that table.

Then Harry said, "I had a squirrel as a pet when I was

young," right in the middle of the group discussing how and why fox hunting had started in the first place. Everyone stopped talking apart from Mother, who kept on talking about how they must have been culled in the past and then realised she was having a conversation on her own, as everyone was staring at Harry.

She wasn't quite sure why but decided to go with the majority and turned her attention to Harry. Nicole, of course, spoke first: "What the hell has that got to do with fox hunting? You are such a weirdo. You always come up with such random subjects when we are talking. Why can't you just engage your brain before you talk?" Harry, of course, was always a good sparring partner and hence the bringing out of the popcorn each time they started.

However, there was no need for that this time as we had a full meal in front of us. G and I rubbed our hands together as if to say, 'This should be a good one', as we hadn't had a good one for a while and realised, we had missed them.

"Well, my little rosebud," said Harry, sarcastically, "we are talking about animals, no? So, I was reminded of my squirrel."

"What kind of crazy logic is that?" said Nicole. "Does that mean each time you start talking about your bloody cars, I can start talking about going on holiday on a plane because that is a mode of transport?"

Now it was Hélène 's turn to chip in. "Well Nicole, I can see his point. We never know where our minds are going to take us and we sometimes find connections with unusual things." Having said this, she turned to Mother for acknowledgement and agreement and Mother always gave it.

Mum nodded. "Yes, I can see what you are saying."

Now it was Alain's turn. "'Don't be ridiculous, you two. Nicole is right. How can you associate fox hunting with having a squirrel as a pet?"

An argument then broke out between Alain and Nicole on one side, Harry, Hélène and Mother on the other. No one spoke louder or more emphatically than Nicole but this time, I think Harry was determined to lead on this. He was actually making some headway and G and I were very proud of him, until he was stopped mid-flow by Alain saying, "Mathematically speaking…"

Alain rarely brought up his mathematics genius, as he was an extremely modest man but he always reverted to it when he felt pushed into a corner, so the moment he started with 'Mathematically speaking…' you knew he was going to floor you with jargon and stuff that may or may not actually be mathematically correct but no one would know this apart from him. Therefore, you couldn't argue with it.

"*Ooooph, Alain, arrête!*" said Hélène. "You always just try and win an argument by saying that."

Yet again, the cacophony that ensued after that, with everyone shouting over each other, was now getting a bit too much for Mother who finally shouted, "Oh, for fox's sake!"

Mother never swore so this stopped everyone dead in their tracks for a few seconds and then, the whole table burst out laughing when we realised what she had said. From that day on, everyone started to use 'for fox's sake' with gay abandon without feeling guilty.

Life on a Postcard No. 82
What A Lovely Surprise

'We four' met on a regular basis. Sometimes G joined us and sometimes Gayem would bring his 'latest' with him. It was just before one of these meetings when there was a knock on the door. It was Freya and Adrian.

"Get in," she said, pointing to the car. "We have a surprise. But we have to stop off and get DK first."

Gayem was surprised too but we all knew it was pointless questioning Freya, so we questioned Adrian instead. But Adrian knew it was pointless telling us, as he would get it in the neck from Freya.

We drove for about half an hour and then arrived at Daisy's Organic Free-Range Farm. We looked at each other. This was nice but why all the secrecy? We disembarked and walked briskly over to a large barn. The farmer met us, smiled and opened the great doors to let us in and there, running amuck, were hundreds, nay, I should go so far as to say *thousands* of chickens. Gayem started shrieking but by now both Freya and I were so used to his shrieking, that we carried on regardless. I certainly couldn't decide what was more painful: the thousands of chickens clucking, or Gayem's shrieking, which was now thankfully drowned out by the chickens.

At the other end of the barn, was a man waiting for us with two garlands in his hands. We tried to walk towards him through the chickens, which took about fifteen minutes as we waded through them, trying not to step on them. However, each time we did we got pecked. Gayem kept asking Freya what this was all about and why she was putting him through this.

"What have I ever done to you other than shower you with love and affection? And this is how you repay me?"

G and I knew instantly what it was all about and though we were excited, we still couldn't help question, why here and like this?

When we reached the garland-holding man, we both congratulated Freya and Adrian and told them it was a lovely surprise. Gayem was still trying to fight his way through the chickens. As we waited for him to make his way through the fowl, Freya explained that the gentleman was a spiritualist and authorised to conduct weddings. If they wanted to make it legal though, they would have to go through a civil ceremony which they were in no hurry to do.

Me: (shouting) "But why here?"

Freya: (Shouting equally loudly) "Each time I had to go for an MRI or a mammogram or an X-ray, they would put the machine on and leave me. There was complete silence and it was not a good silence, so I wanted to get married surrounded by noise and among the animals that produce my favourite food!"

Me: (sarcastically) "Okay, yes. That makes *perfect* sense."

The man with the garlands started the ceremony. None of us could hear a word but I don't think any of us were interested in what he had to say. We were too busy, hopping from one foot to another, while the chickens pecked at our heels, toes and ankles. He then handed Freya and Adrian a garland each and as they started to garland each other, I turned to G and said,

"That garland... it isn't? It can't be! Surely, it's not? I can't believe it!" It was made out of marijuana leaves and flowers!

We exited the barn not a moment too soon. Any longer and Gayem would have killed at least one chicken who had taken a shine to him and kept trying to fly onto his shoulder.

We were then ushered into the farmhouse and there, on a large oak table, was a spread of the greatest variety of egg products I had ever seen: egg canapés, egg sandwiches, egg on toast, stuffed eggs, scrambled eggs, egg pâté and finally the wedding cake in the shape of an egg.

"I love egg," said Freya, to the farmer and his wife.

"I'm so glad you cleared that up," said the farmer.

None of us, apart from Freya, have been able to eat eggs since.

Life on a Postcard No. 83
Back to The Missionary Position Again

Both G and I had talked about how we were going to wait at least five years to have a baby. We wanted to see more of the world, if that was possible. We wanted to do all we could before we had children, so that we could devote all our time to them when they came. However, a trip to South Africa changed that.

G was asked to travel to South Africa by a sewage company that turned sewage water into drinking water by putting it through thousands of filters and purifications. He had done some photographs for them as a favour, since the owner was a distant cousin and had done such a creative job, that the Marketing Director said G was the first person he had met that could make 'shit look sexy'.

He was off to Johannesburg and I went with him. When we landed, I noticed huge boxes being offloaded from the luggage belt. I asked the lady standing next to them what they were for. "They're for an orphanage here. We make a trip once a year to bring supplies donated by the very generous British people."

I found out where the orphanage was and convinced G to come with me the next day. This orphanage housed children of HIV parents who were either dead or dying. They had been tested for AIDS and some were infected and some had been given the all-clear. The ones who were unaffected, were put up for adoption and there was already a long waiting list. Yes, I know what you are thinking and no, we did *not* do a Madonna and bring one back with us.

But that trip seemed to have the same effect on us both.

On the flight back, I turned to G as we took off and he took one look at me and we both spoke in perfect harmony. "Let's have a baby," we said.

I had always thought that once I decided to have a baby, the next month, miraculously, that would happen. When you have been told all your life that you are a miracle, then you tend to expect miracles to happen to you.

No such luck.

A few months went by without me even batting an eyelid, as I was so sure the next month would be the one.

After six months, I decided that perhaps we needed to get ourselves tested, just to make sure everything was working and fluids were flowing in the right direction at the correct speed and frequency.

I had to have a swab and G had to give a sample. He could *produce* his sample in a pot and bring it in with him if it was within half an hour. But I had to look forward to the indignity of having something shoved up me, legs spread and a sample taken.

Before I went in, I wanted to make sure I was completely fragrant and sanitised, so I nipped into the loo and used wet wipes I had brought in my handbag and gave it one last wipe.

To my horror the person taking the swab turned out to be a man. I nearly turned on my heel and ran. Sensing my horror, he said, "Don't worry. I usually have this reaction from most of my patients but I can assure you, it's all in a day's work."

Yes, thank you, I thought. *That really does make me feel a whole lot better.*

I climbed nervously onto the bed and he discreetly put a sheet over me and I peeled off my knickers. He then lifted the sheet gently, poised with the ghastly contraption in hand which was going to prise my vagina open as wide as a snap dragon trying to catch a fly and then... he just burst out laughing.

Well, I have had some strange reactions to it in the past but my vagina couldn't be *that* bloody funny to look at.

He then tried to suppress his laughter while he spoke: "I've seen them in some odd places before but this is the strangest place I have ever come across one!" I looked down and there, neatly secured to my vagina lips, was a first-class stamp! It must have been at the bottom of my bag and got stuck to the wet wipe that I had wiped myself with!

I sat bolt upright, jumped off the bed and ran out as fast as I could, pulling my knickers up as I stumbled out. I could hear him calling after me, apologising, saying he was very sorry but he was so shocked he didn't know how to react.

I made another appointment and this time insisted it was with a woman.

Life on a Postcard No. 84
If I Wanted Insanity, I Would Ask for It

Finally, both tests were back and apparently, I was ovulating for all of England and part of South Wales and G's sperm count was higher than Zuckerman's bank balance.

Therefore, the doctor told us, we just weren't timing it right.

Everyone now felt it was appropriate to give us advice.

Mum: "Just relax, darling. If you are tense it will never happen."

Dad: "Don't worry, darling. Look how you were born! If that can happen, anything can happen. You know when your mother conceived…"

Both Mum and I, gave Dad the dirtiest look we could each time he started to tell that story, as it reminded us of the wedding speech and he knew to zip it straightaway.

Alain: "Lots of sex. Ha! Ha! Ha!"

Nicole: "If you have a lump of sugar in the morning followed by vinegar and then three tablespoons of olive oil, apparently the sperm reacts to that very well."

Harry: "My mamma always used to say that you must sleep facing east and that will help with conception."

Gayem: "What are you looking at me for? I don't even stick it in that hole."

Cousin A: "Charlotte, first of all you need to have sex as many times as you can when you are ovulating. I used to call Tris home from work in the middle of the day because my temperature was just right. He did grumble about that quite a bit but it's worth it. Then you must — absolutely *must* — lie with your legs straight up in the air for ten minutes after sex."

Mr Raju: "Charlottie, you must not leave any stone unturned." ('Finally!' I thought, 'someone is going to make some sense.' I waited with bated breath) "You must first pray to Lord Ganesh. Then, you must do puja to the goddess Laxmi. Then, you must start to follow Sai Baba. He will look after you. Then, just to be on the safe side, go to Church and light a candle. Then, also ask an Imam to pray for you. Why not? They can also help when needed."

Freya sent me a card: on the outside there were two sperm swimming. One sperm was saying to the other sperm, 'Are we there yet?' When we opened the card, on the inside, the other sperm answered, 'No, we haven't even passed the tonsils yet.'

Hélène was the one who was the most concerned as she *really* wanted a grandchild and seemed even more impatient than me and even more dejected than I was, when I didn't conceive month after month. She would ring me each month when my period was due and say, "*Quoi?*" I would then tell her I had got my period and she would exclaim, "*Merde!*"

I would then comfort her, tell her we would try again and not to get too disappointed; that there was always next month and the month after that. She was irritable and snappy. Finally, she could take it no longer and said, "You must go see my friend. She is a nutritionist and healer and she can test you for all sorts of allergies and deficiencies and give you special vitamins and tablets to ensure your body is ready for fertilisation to take place."

Life on a Postcard No. 85
Just Fresh Air, Thank You

Her name was Isabella and she was a lovely lady with a hearty laugh. We arrived there at 8 a.m., as I had been asked to be there, to deliver my first wee of the morning, so she could test it.

I walked into the clinic impersonating John Wayne's walk and made it to the loo just in time, managing to grab a little pot being held out by Isabella's assistant as I made a mad dash to the toilet. The pot was too small to hold a whole night's worth of wee, so I weed all over my hand, which was not pleasant but I didn't envy the person who was testing that sample, either.

Firstly, Isabella said she was going to test me for food intolerances. She put a sensor onto my middle and pressed hard, keeping it there for what seemed like a month while the machine it was attached to rumbled, then jigged about, then started churning out some graphs on a piece of paper. I felt like I was in a scene from *Dr Who*. Finally, I was given my finger back and had to massage it to get the blood flowing again.

Then, I was given an acupuncture session which ended up being more of a competition of who could come up with the best 'prick' jokes. I guess I only have myself to blame as I started it by saying to G, "Well, darling, they did say it was only one small, little prick that would get me pregnant and they weren't lying."

Let me give you an example of some of the others:

G: "One little prick and it will all be over."

Me: "That's what you said the first time we had sex."

G to Isabella: "Aren't you putting them in the wrong places?"

Me: "Isn't that what I said to you the first time we had sex?"

G: "How many pricks does it take to make a woman pregnant?"

Me: "In your case, just one, darling."

And so, they continued.

Finally, it was all over and that was half a day of my life I would never get back again.

The verdict was in. Isabella sat down with us to go through the results of the intolerance / allergy tests.

She looked at sheets and sheets of paper that had been produced by the *Dr Who* machine, shaking her head, tut-tutting, raising her eyebrows and drawing in deep breaths through her mouth, like she was sucking hard on a straw that had something stuck in it.

Later the same day... she looked at the summary of all these sheets. She *hmmmmmed* at this sheet and crooked her head from side to side a few times.

Then she finally spoke.

"Right," she said, "in order for you to get pregnant you need to cut out all the foods your body is intolerant to."

"These are the foods that are in the *Red* Zone. You must absolutely *not* eat them:

Eggs, cheese, all jams, milk, yoghurt, and any other dairy products you can think of, beef, pork, fish, chicken, tea, coffee, chocolate, any type of confectionary, sugar and this includes natural sugars as well, so no fruit at all. You can, however, drink soya milk.

"These foods that are in the *Amber* Zone, you can eat in moderation about once a week: bread and any yeast products, pasta, rice, or any other carbohydrates, including potatoes.

"These in the *Green* Zone you are neither allergic to nor intolerant to them." Both G and I waited with bated breath to see what I could eat and drink for the foreseeable future: Water.

"You can drink lots of water and it won't harm you."

"What about fresh air?" I asked, trying not to let the sarcasm completely take over.

We left there feeling quite dejected as Isabella had insisted that if I did not do what she said, I would not get pregnant. She had also given me vitamins and minerals and laden us with so many supplements, that we both resembled orangutans walking back to the car.

Life on a Postcard No. 86
Now It's Getting Annoying

I threw the summary in the bin as I did not believe in all that intolerance stuff; after eating magic mushrooms and surviving, nothing I ate now could possibly stop me getting pregnant. However, I did take the vitamins and mineral supplements dutifully and actually began to see a difference. My hair was nice and bouncy and I felt more energised... well, maybe a bit too energised, as G said it was getting a bit worrying as I was so bubbly 'all the bloody time'!

But the one thing the tabs were not doing was getting me pregnant.

Everyone around me was more tense than I was and started to know my cycle better than I did. I was called all hours of the day and night to ask if I had done this or done that and they even started to argue among themselves.

I finally called a conference.

Attendees: My parents, Hélène, Alain, Freya, Adrian, Gayem, Nicole, Harry and G, plus Cousin A who dialled in from Hong Kong.

"Now the first thing I would like to say is that you all need to *stop*!"

"Alicia, stop calling me up at 11 p.m. and asking me if I've had sex yet that day, as my temperature levels were at their peak."

"Hélène, stop stressing each month when my period is due, calling me ten times a day and then putting the phone down. I know it's you." Hélène tried to protest. "Hélène, your mobile number comes up on my phone! Don't you know that?" She didn't know that; any type of technology was not her strong point.

"Alain, stop being bullied by Hélène and pretending to bump into me at Waitrose halfway through my cycle to find out how many times I've had sex in the last two days."

"Mum, stop telling me to relax! I *am* relaxed but everyone else is stressing me out!"

"Nicole, stop looking up on the internet and giving me strange pieces of advice like drinking ginger water while standing on my head when I've just had sex."

"Harry, I love your mother, but please tell her to stop sending me strange and wonderful Italian traditions that *absolutely* work. Trust me: bathing in a bath of fennel and goat's milk before sex is not going to do it."

"Gayem, why the bloody hell are you here? You have been as useful as a vagina is to a homosexual." Gayem started to protest, saying he didn't know why he was there either and had been forced to come, but I just carried on.

"Adrian, I know you are trying to cheer me up by sending me silly jokes but please stop, as my womb can only take so many. Some of them are funny but some are just not so, like the one you sent me yesterday. Am I really more likely to get pregnant if my husband wears boxers rather than briefs? Yes, but I'll have an even better chance if he doesn't wear anything at all? Really?"

"Freya, stop sending me silly cards."

"Guillaume, stop saying, "Oh no, not again!" when I tell you we have to have sex. By the way we need to do it again in twenty minutes."

It was Adrian who spoke first. "Okay, joking aside, this is the best advice I can give you: sperm takes forty-eight hours to get to the womb. You only ovulate for twenty-four hours, so have as much intercourse as you can twenty-four hours *before* you start to ovulate. In order to check to see when you are about to ovulate, buy the sticks. They are the most accurate."

He then calmly picked up his cup of tea and continued to drink it, while we all stared at him in absolute bewilderment.

Freya looked at him with great pride but of course didn't want to show it. "Where did you get all that from?" she asked.

"I looked it up in case we found ourselves in the same situation as these two," he said, gesturing towards us.

We all knew that meant he really did want to try for a baby but Freya was having none of it. "Well, that day will come the day I wake up in the morning and say, "Adrian, I am sick of eggs"."

We all knew that day would never come.

Life on a Postcard No. 87
Rub Its Tummy for Luck

Wanting to leave no stone unturned, we even tried Adrian's advice and to be fair to the others, they left us alone for a while.

Gayem had decided to throw a party as Truly Scrumptious had attained her Level Four in swimming and he wanted to celebrate this. TS had been taking swimming lessons for a while, as it helped with her arthritis apparently. It was a very gay affair in every way. All friends were encouraged to bring their pets. There was absolute mayhem everywhere as Gayem chased after them, trying to clean up the wee and poo, while he kept saying to himself, 'It seemed like a good idea at the time'.

I was talking to Freya about the latest article I had written for a magazine that wanted a different take on married life and we were laughing about how I was jolly well giving them that, when I noticed G and Adrian talking and looking at us.

On the way home I asked G what that was all about and G said Adrian had come up to him at the party to say, "I know you probably don't want to tell anyone just yet but I wanted to be the first to congratulate you."

G had asked him what he was on about and Adrian said, "Charlotte is finally pregnant, isn't she?" G had said not that he was aware of and Adrian said he had noticed I was subconsciously rubbing my tummy as I was talking, which apparently was one of the signs someone was pregnant. We both laughed about it, feeling very sorry for Adrian as he really had swallowed the book on pregnancy and yet there was more chance of Father being allowed to speak in public again, than there was of Freya agreeing to try for a baby. And Father was *never* going to be allowed to speak in public again!

A week later, G was away in Hong Kong on a shoot, when I realised, I was two days late but I didn't want to get my hopes up, so didn't take the test. Freya knew this and kept telling me to take it but I wouldn't. G got back home and at 3 a.m. on the third day, the phone rang.

It was Freya, shouting down the phone, "Take the bloody test! None of us can get any sleep!" She then slammed the phone down.

G slept through the call and I decided, as I was up, I might as well do it.

I did a wee on the pregnancy stick as usual but something felt different this time.

Even before that second line went blue, I knew it. But actually, seeing it turn blue was still magical. I could barely breathe! How was I going to tell G? I had been planning to give the stick to him as a present and had even bought the exact size box to put it in but how could I wait till the morning? I wouldn't be able to sleep! And I would be damned if I was going to let my best laid plans go to waste.

I put the stick in the box and then woke him up.

"Sorry darling," I said apologetically, "but I bought this for you and really want you to have it now."

"For goodness sake, can it not wait till morning?"

"It really can't," I said.

He woke up blurry eyed and opened the box, picked up the stick and tried to focus but even though I could tell he couldn't actually see what it was, or the blue lines, he had seen enough of the sticks to know.

He looked at me and said, "When did you...?"

"Five minutes ago," I said. He threw the box aside and hugged me tight. He was shaking.

We decided we had to tell everyone right then and there but we just couldn't face all the questions at 3 a.m., so we decided to let Freya do it.

I rang Freya. She just picked up the phone and didn't speak.

All I said was, "Yes, yes, yes."

"I knew it," she said. "Adrian told me you were but you didn't know it."

She said that with so much pride, which was really sweet because Freya didn't show any emotion about anyone, especially pride.

G and I suddenly remembered the conversation Adrian had had with him the week before, regarding me rubbing my tummy. He was right! He really had swallowed the book!

I asked Freya if she could tell the rest as we couldn't bear all the questions at what was now 4 a.m. She said she would but would not entertain any banter. Little did I realise, she really meant it.

Apparently, this is how the calls went:

My parents

'Ring Ring'

A groggy Mother picked up the phone and mumbled into it, about who was calling at this time.

Freya: "Just wanted to let you know Charlotte is pregnant."

Mum: "*What*?"

Freya put the phone down.

314

Hélène and Alain:

Hélène picked up, sounding crisp and clear, not even questioning the 4 a.m. call.

Hélène: "*Allo?*"

Freya: "Just wanted to let you know Charlotte is pregnant."

Hélène: "*Mon dieu! Mais...*"

Freya put down the phone.

Cousin Alicia:

CA: "Why are you calling me, Freya? I haven't bothered Charlotte for four days now."

Freya:" Just wanted to let you know Charlotte is pregnant."

CA: "Bed knobs and barnacles! How did...?"

Freya put down the phone.

Nicole and Harry:

Nicole picked up the phone and was already complaining to Harry saying, "'It must be one of your bloody friends as no one would call me at this hour. Who is this?"

Freya: "Just wanted to let you know Charlotte is pregnant."

Nicole burst into tears and was about to speak.

Freya put down the phone.

DK (aka Gayem)

DK: "Frey, what the...?"

Freya: "Just wanted to let you know Charlotte is pregnant."

DK: "Am so pleased for her but I am so upset as Ms Truly has been constipated and..."

Freya put down the phone.

Apparently, now not only did everyone remember where

they were and what they were doing when JFK died but now the same went for when they heard I was pregnant.

We turned our phones off and had a peaceful three hours' sleep before we had to answer all the questions and listen to all the comments, accusations and moans.

Mum: "Honestly, darling, your own mother… depriving me of the one conversation a mother waits to have with her daughter. How could you?" Then the emotional blackmail and drama kicked in. "The one person you should have called yourself; your own mother. You are my only child…"

Hélène: The French can do drama as well as the English, sometimes even better depending on the time of day. If you catch them after their habitual glass of wine during lunch, then you not only get it with both barrels but laden with guilt and a dollop of *solidarité* on top! "Guillaume, how could you, my son? We are your family after all. Vera Lynne and I are very upset." Nowadays, we rarely heard one talk without mentioning the other.

Cousin A: "I am so pleased for you but you could have called me yourself! The amount of time and energy I have invested in this pregnancy, I…"

Nicole: Burst into tears as soon as she heard my voice. "I can't believe I'm going to be an aunt. I thought we were close. Why didn't you call me yourself?"

DK: "Charlotte, do you know Frey called me at 4 a.m. — no, I think it must have been 4.15 a.m. — to tell me you were preggers. Congratulations! But do you know Truly hasn't been for three days and I have been so worried…"

Life on a Postcard No. 88
A Scan in Time

All went well from there and though I could barely see any difference in me, I could feel it. Then, at seven weeks, I started bleeding. I was at home and about to sit down to a large bowl of *Dulce de leche* ice cream at 10 a.m. It was the only time I was going to be able to do that and not feel terribly guilty, so I'd promised myself I would eat whatever I liked when I was pregnant. I started to feel a bit of wetness and when I looked down, I was bleeding.

I didn't want to call G, as he was in the middle of a shoot so I called Mother to meet me at the hospital, in case I needed some moral support when they told me I had lost the baby. She, of course, then called her new BFF, Hélène. Since the wedding they had been inseparable as they realised, they seemed to have some sort of magical powers when they joined forces and together, were a force to reckoned with but apart they were not as powerful.

Hélène then needed the support of Alain who, in turn, did not want to have to deal with 'the Force' (Mother and Hélène), as he called them, on his own, so he wanted the support of Father. The fathers also felt the need to call Nicole and Harry, who said they would meet them at the hospital.

The mothers decided in their wisdom they should let Cousin A. know and the fathers tried to override this decision but their decision to override was overridden by the overidees! Cousin A insisted on being put on Facetime and bullied Mother into picking Gayem up on the way, as he was her commander-in-chief. If she couldn't be there, he was the next best thing, as he would report back faithfully to her and do her bidding when it came to making decisions. Gayem was in the middle of his pore-cleansing cycle and shrieked when he saw all four of them at his door, with Cousin A still on Facetime.

He could never decide who he was more scared of, Cousin A or Freya but he decided to call Freya on the way. The scene that met me as I was waiting to be scanned was, in itself, enough to cause a miscarriage. I was expecting one mother, perhaps slightly concerned, who would sit and hold my hand, and instead, I was faced with two mothers, two fathers and a patchwork doll, as they didn't give Gayem enough time to take off all of his face mask.

They were shortly followed by a squabbling Nicole and Harry, as Harry had decided to park the car in the car park, while Nicole felt it was an emergency and he should have parked in one of the ambulance bays.

Harry: "How can you expect me to park in an ambulance bay when I am not an ambulance?"

Nicole: "Don't be ridiculous. Those bays are for emergencies and if this is not an emergency then I really don't know what is."

Harry: "What is wrong with you, Nicole? Every time I feel you get more and more unreasonable."

My first words to them were, "Anyone else?"

"Oh, yes," said Gayem, "we have Alicia on Facetime and Freya's on her way."

"You have got to be kidding me!" It was me who shrieked this time.

When the horrified nurse arrived to scan me, she kept her composure as I was trying to do and said quietly and slowly, "Is any one of you the father?"

It then suddenly struck me how furious G would be if he knew they were all here except him. Yet I didn't want him to know till I was sure.

I said, "He isn't here at the moment."

The nurse said quite indignantly, "Well only one of you can come in with the mum." They all (except Gayem) looked at me expectantly, like little children waiting to be chosen for a game.

Gayem always seemed to be dragged to these things against his will but loved to be dramatic about them afterwards. For the first time he didn't make this about him and his patchwork face.

I said, "Well, if Freya were here, I would probably take her in, as none of you deserve to come in with me, especially you, Mum." But in the end, I did take Mother in because I knew she couldn't help herself when it came to Hélène; she was as addicted to her as I was to the smell of petrol.

When lying on the bed, yet again with my legs apart, the nurse told me to relax. I was now really wishing I had called G. She told me she would need to do an internal scan as it was only seven weeks and ultrasound wouldn't pick up anything. Within ten seconds of her shoving the scan up me, Mum and I heard something that sounded like soft bullets being shot out of a machine gun.

"What's that?" I asked.

"That," said the nurse, "is your baby's heartbeat."

We then saw a tiny kidney bean and the nurse said, "There it is. You have nothing to worry about."

I burst into tears, not so much from the relief but out of sadness because G wasn't here to share it with me. As we were marvelling at the kidney bean, someone burst into the room and the nurse jumped up to protest. It was Freya. She stuck out her hand and said to the nurse, "Relax, sister. I've had breast cancer." Pointing to her left breast, she said, "Veteran of one mastectomy, so keep your hair on. I lost mine many times but that's another story."

Freya was shortly followed by G! The nurse stared to protest again and Freya said, "Chill! He's the father."

This time I started to say, "How did you...?"

"I called him," Freya said. "Shoot or no shoot, he needed to be here."

And she was right.

Freya continued, "And when I heard the whole bloody French *and* British battalions were going to be here, how could *he* not be? What were you thinking, Charlotte?"

I started to explain but she put her hand up as if to say: Don't worry, I know exactly what you mean. That was the other amazing thing about Freya; she could hear things you don't even say. At this point, Freya gently took Mother out of the room and G and I were able to have a first sight of our baby together. The nurse reassured us there was nothing to worry about but just to give myself a bit of time to relax before I got up. She then let the rest in. I discharged the lot of them straight away with a flea in each ear, except Freya of course, who I thanked for being the sensible one.

As she was leaving, she flung something on my bed and said, "This is all your fault!" as she walked out the door.

G picked it up for me and we both stared at it in absolute amazement, lost for words, not wanting to even speak because there in our hands we were holding something very familiar; something we had both seen only seven weeks ago — a pregnancy test with two clear blue lines. Only this time it was Freya's.

Life on a Postcard No. 89
Bloomin' Marvellous!

No one was more shocked than Freya over her pregnancy but I think at some point, she must have relented and realised that she would have to have one, though Adrian kept talking about having four. She eventually made him sign an agreement and had it authorised by a notary public that he wouldn't pressure her to have any more. You think I'm joking, but she did.

"One is all I can manage to push out. I can't even keep plants and goldfish alive, how am I going to manage with a child?"

We all reassured her she would.

During my first trimester I had dreadful morning sickness and each morning, I woke up feeling like I had been on the choppy Pacific for a month, on a dinghy, with no oars.

Freya breezed through it, eating her usual full English fry-up each morning and in usual Freya fashion, it didn't affect her life one little bit. "The only thing I miss is my weed." After she was given the all-clear, she started having a joint or two once in a while but as soon as she knew she was pregnant she stopped.

I actually lost weight during my first trimester but then the moment the morning sickness stopped, I started to pile on the pounds. I went through the awful stage where my tummy was bloated but I still didn't look pregnant and just looked like I'd eaten all the pies at an all-you-can-eat pie buffet. So, I spent weeks sticking my stomach out and supporting my back so everyone knew I was pregnant and not just fat.

Then, I started taking eating seriously towards the end of my second trimester and started to treat it as a national sport. I woke up thinking of food and what I was going to eat for breakfast. No sooner had the last morsel of cereal gone down my throat, than I was thinking of my mid-morning snack. Sometimes I didn't even wait till mid-morning and it would be eaten early morning. Then, it got to the stage where there were no set timings for when I was going to eat. Each meal and snack rolled into the next and before I knew it, I was swimming one day and a whale hunter tried to harpoon me.

However, this didn't stop me in my quest for being the largest pregnant woman on earth and it was during the second trimester, that I had to be airlifted everywhere. Now, I was just eating for the sake of eating. I was literally trying to get down as much food as I could in nine months, as I knew I would never be able to do this again.

Everything reminded me of food: buildings reminded me of ice-cream cones, writing reminded me of basil leaves. Basil leaves and grapefruit seemed to be my cravings and while those wouldn't have been too bad, I also stuffed my face with everything else in sight.

Freya was able to eat all she wanted and never put on any weight and being pregnant didn't change that.

Life on a Postcard No. 90
What If It Traumatises the Baby?

The first time we saw our baby it was a tiny little kidney bean. The next scan we had was at twelve weeks and this time we saw the head and the body; it was already almost formed. G could not take his eyes off it. It even had tiny little fingernails! As we watched the scan, it put its hand up to its head and scratched it! We squeezed each other's hands so tightly, we both yelped at the same time!

However, from that moment on, G started acting quite strangely around me. He acted like I was a Ming vase and he was my caretaker. For a few days it was quite sweet when he came running, each time he heard a sound, or saw me try to reach up for something. Then, it started to get slightly annoying, so we had to sit down and have a chat.

"G," I said, "I am not an invalid. I am not sick. I am extremely healthy as you can see and could eat my body fat for a year and still not run out of sustenance, so please, stop worrying about me."

That seemed to calm him down for a bit but now I noticed that each time we got a bit amorous with each other and were about to make love, he would either start yawning, saying he was exhausted, or that he had to get up early for a shoot, or he had a cramp in his leg and finally, when he ran out of excuses, he came up with, "Not tonight, I have a headache!"

That was it!

Me: "No, no, mister. Hold on a second. *You* don't have the

headaches, I do! Now what's going on?"

G: "Okay. I'm scared."

Me: "Sacred of what?"

G: "Scared it will hurt the baby."

Me: "How can it hurt the baby? Now, darling, I know you are no cigar stub, but you ain't that big!"

G: "Well, what if it pokes the baby? What if you miscarry?"

Me: "What? Seriously, honey, you are not *that* big! Even if you were, there is no way into the womb from there unless you have a sharp needle on the end of that thing!"

G: "Okay, I take your point. But what if the baby sees it coming towards it and gets traumatised? It has eyes now, you know."

Me: "Yes, it does but they are not open and I can assure you, it will not see your penis!"

Finally, he gave in — just once! And I tell you, I have had some strange sexual experiences in my time but none like that! Making love to a traumatised, nervous dad-to-be was a bizarre experience.

Life on a Postcard No. 91
What's in A Name?

It was time to choose a name. Freya had already decided if she had a boy it would be called 'Heath', as she thought she'd conceived on Hampstead Heath. Nobody wanted to know any more details than that. If she had a girl, it would be called Xania. Please, don't ask: I really don't even think that's a name. It was probably the technical name of a species of weed.

Everyone felt they could jump on the bandwagon with names for my baby. Not sure why it was one rule for me and one rule for Freya. She was more forceful than me, I guess, and it wasn't her mad family, I suppose.

"We need it to sound both French and English," said Mother. Hélène agreed.

Names were sourced from the depths of France, from the ancient scripts of Anglosaxon times, from dictionaries, from everywhere.

G and I had two criteria: it needed to sound nice and it needed to be unusual.

French names were suggested, from Adelise right the way to Zoelie and there was no dearth of English ones either, from Adeldra to Zavrina.

None seemed to appeal to us. None really grabbed us where we said, 'Yes! That's it!' So we waited, hoping divine intervention would play a part and it did.

We happened to be watching a cheesy rom com one day and were quite bored of it but exhausted and pregnant, I couldn't be bothered to even get up or switch it off. Then it happened: a new character was introduced to the storyline. Her name was Lilya. We sat up, looked at each other and said, "That's it!"

We loved the name and while it sounded French, we doubted it was and looked it up. It was Persian — close enough — and the word meant 'brightest star.' So, Lilya it was but now we needed a bit of English in there.

G said, "Her second name really does need to sound like an English Rose." We stopped dead in our tracks, looked at each other and both shouted, "Lilya Rose!"

Now, here's the bizarre part: not one single person who felt they had a say in what name we called our baby, actually disagreed! Quite amazing! They all loved the name. Strangely enough, we never chose a boy's name as we were so convinced it would be a girl.

Life on a Postcard No. 92
Are All Babies Cute?

I insisted that Freya attended all the antenatal classes with me, even though she really didn't think she needed to. "I don't work with recipes, I don't ask for directions, I don't obey the law. Why do I need a bunch of stuck-up old midwives to tell me what to do with my baby? I will play it by ear, suck it and see and take it as it comes."

I assured her she would need all the help she could get.

During our first antenatal, the midwife went around the room asking each of us in turn what our greatest fear was for our baby. All the other mothers said they were worried it would be disabled, or sick, or there would be a problem at the birth. As she went around the circle of expectant mothers and they came up with their predictable concerns, the midwife nodded and 'Ummed' in agreement.

As the time got closer for me to tell them what my greatest fear was, Freya leant over to me and said, "Are you going to tell them the truth?"

"No, of course not," I said. "I can't do that, they'll think I'm mad."

"Who the bloody hell cares?" Freya scoffed. "Look at the lot of them. Do you really think you're going to forge great friendships with any of this lot? You will never see them again, well, apart from that one with the humungous bosoms. We might want to keep in with her. She looks like she could breastfeed a whole maternity ward with those boobs."

As the midwife got round to me, I kept telling myself not to tell them the truth. "Don't say it, don't say it. Just say something like your greatest concern is that it will be unhealthy. Play it safe and say that or play it safer and say my greatest concern is that the birth won't go smoothly."

"And what about you, Charlotte?" the midwife said, breaking my train of thought mid-flow. "My greatest concern is that my child will be ugly."

That's it! I said it. There you go. It was done.

Everyone stared at me for a few seconds and then burst into fits of laughter. The midwife said, through her spurts of snorts, "Don't be silly, Charlotte, every child is gorgeous and adorable."

Freya and I shook our heads symbiotically, "Uh-uh," we tutted.

"No way," said Freya. "I have seen some ugly babies. Just the other day, when I came for my routine check-up, there was a woman in the queue ahead of me. Her baby was in a pram. When the mother turned around, I nearly gave birth in the line. He was UG-UR-LY!" she said, in her best Southern American accent.

Life on a Postcard No. 93
It's A Boy! It's A Girl! It's A Baby!

At twenty weeks, both Freya and I booked our scans together. I was desperate to find out whether I was having a girl or a boy. Freya said she would be content just knowing it was human.

G and I were nervous as the nurse started the scan. She started at the head.

Nurse: "Look at that lovely formation of the skull."

Us: "Yes, but is it a girl?"

Nurse: "Everything seems very normal with head area."

Us: "Yes but can we just go a bit further down?"

Nurse: "Look at the chambers of the heart; look how well they are moving. You have a very healthy baby here."

Us: "Yes but *what* baby is it?"

Nurse: "Well, the little nails have come out and... oh my goodness, did you see that? It scratched its head."

Us: "Yes, that's all very lovely but is it a girl?"

The nurse gave us the dirtiest look we had ever seen. A look that said, 'Here I am, telling you what a healthy baby you have, about how well it's forming and developing and how lucky you are and all you are bothered about, is whether it's a girl. Do you know how many parents I have had to tell during such scans that their babies are not very healthy? And here you have a wonderfully healthy baby and you can't be bothered'.

Now you may very well ask how we got all that from just one look but I promise you we did. She was very expressive.

The nurse had now finally approached the nether regions and moved around every angle, making sure she got it right for the two lunatic parents who were in front of her. She finally looked at us, smiled broadly and said, "It's a little gorgeous baby girl!"

We couldn't contain ourselves; we were so delighted.

We met Adrian and Freya outside and she said, "You go first."

I couldn't be bothered to argue and said, "Yes, it's a girl! And you?" Adrian who couldn't take the smile off his face was about to speak, when Freya shoved her palm into his face.

"Pah! We are delighted to say it's at least in the human form," Freya said. "Who cares what else it is?" Notwithstanding the fact that she had the right attitude, I gave her my sternest look. "Okay, it's a boy," she finally admitted.

Life on a Postcard No. 94
It Won't Happen to You

We were both approximately six months now. Freya noticed that she had felt very little movement in about twelve hours or so, which was unlike Freya as she usually didn't notice anything. Adrian took her to the hospital but she called me while they were waiting for a scan, as he was boring a hole in the carpet by his constant pacing and Freya said she needed me to take control of him.

When I got there, they were already in the room being scanned. Freya wanted me to be there. We all held our breath as the nurse looked at the baby in the womb. She moved the scan around and looked at it from many different angles. Freya and Adrian were looking intently at the baby on the screen. I was looking at the nurse's expression. I could see her desperately trying to find something, listen for something. She was listening for the heartbeat. She couldn't hear it. I knew I couldn't be there when she broke the news: 1. Because I wanted them to hear it together alone and 2. I didn't think I would be able to stay composed.

I said I desperately needed to wee and left them alone.

I sat down on a chair outside away from the room and sobbed quietly. Passers-by stopped to ask if was okay but I didn't respond. Finally, I got up and ran to the loo. I thought my throwing-up days were over during my pregnancy but I threw up, like I had never thrown up before.

As I was leaving the toilet the nurse said, "I've been

looking for you. Freya would like to see you."

"They say I have to give birth to it. They will induce me tomorrow. Please speak to Adrian before you leave. I can't console him. And Charlotte, I don't want you to worry. This won't happen to you."

"Well, you can never say never but…" I said.

"It won't," she said. "I can assure you."

Yet again like with the cancer, when Freya was going through the worst possible times in her life, she reverted to her couldn't care less attitude, which was her greatest defence mechanism. As I left the room to find Adrian, her final throwaway comment to me was, "You know I didn't want a baby anyway, so it's for the best."

Maybe it was all the hormones raging inside me, maybe it was the shock, maybe it was the fear it might happen to me but it was definitely rage and anger at her not accepting the situation she was in, that made me react the way I did.

She needed to accept this; not just acceptance for herself but for Adrian who needed her support and *not* her coldness, in order to protect herself. This time she *had* to acknowledge the pain.

"Fuck you! Fuck you! Fuck you!" I shrieked, not just shouted, not just yelled, but shrieked. This brought Adrian running back into the room but that didn't stop me from grabbing her arm in a complete blind rage and propping her up to look into a small mirror that was opposite her bed.

"Look at you!" I continued to shriek. My voice now broke into a cough. "Just look at you! You've just had a miscarriage and are about to give birth to your stillborn baby." By now I was shrieking, coughing and sobbing all at the same time. Even when pregnant and in a blind rage, women can multitask so well.

"Let yourself grieve. If there was ever a time to give yourself permission to grieve, this is it! Do it for him," I said, pointing to Adrian, "even if you don't want to do it for yourself. You owe it to him."

She yanked her arm away from my vice-like grip, as by now my nails were digging into her flesh. She got up from the bed, stood in the middle of the room and looked at each of us in turn.

"You don't understand. It's all my fault. I know now that the cancer was my fault and this is also my fault. I smoked so much weed before I got cancer and I know I stopped when I got pregnant but I had a joint a week ago. I missed it so much. So you see, I killed it. It's my fault. Now do you understand?"

For a split second the expression on Adrian's face said, 'How *could* you?' But all credit to him, it only lasted a few seconds and then he was back to his usually supportive self.

We both tried to reassure her there was no guarantee that was the case. However, we'd achieved what we'd needed to. There in the middle of the room, she looked at herself in the mirror and large teardrops stared to roll down her cheeks. Adrian walked across the room and cradled her gently.

She pushed him away and shouted at us, "Do you know what my name means? Do you know what Freya means?" We shook our heads. "Freya is the Norse god of love and fertility. I am anything but that."

Adrian put his arms around her again and this time wouldn't let go, even though she resisted.

I walked out slowly, closing the door behind me.

Life on a Postcard No. 95
No Mother Should Go Through This

Baby Heath was born the next day. Freya refused to have me there, the doctors refused to have me there, so I waited outside the hospital. I was literally banned from the whole ward. It was almost like they had invisible pictures of my mugshot around, as each time I even approached the ward I was told, 'Now you know you shouldn't be here.'

So, I sat outside and held G's hand and cried continuously from the time Freya went in until the time it was over. I was not allowed to see Heath but I could see Freya.

As I started to enter the room, something stopped me from going further. What would I want if I were her? Would I want to see my friend with a healthy baby inside her, about to deliver it in a few months' time? The answer was no.

I wanted to see her and hug her and tell her everything would be all right, even though I knew it wouldn't for ages and ages and I wanted to be with her and comfort her but I knew she really shouldn't see me at this time.

I questioned myself over and over again as to whether I was yet again running away from a situation I couldn't cope with, as I had done with the Modis but this time, I was sure I was doing this for her and not me.

I left the hospital and rang her. She picked up and without waiting for me to speak, she said, "I understand and you're doing the right thing; I know you're doing it to protect me." At that moment in time, I couldn't have had more admiration for anyone.

Freya didn't want a funeral but Adrian wanted the baby buried, somewhere they could both go to grieve. I didn't go to the burial. The people who had constantly annoyed me during my conception, during my pregnancy, like Mother, ma-in-law, even Cousin A, all called and this time, all of them seemed to know exactly what to say — absolutely nothing.

That is just what I needed; for them to say nothing at all.

They buried Heath in a tiny, little graveyard near Hampstead Heath. G stayed at home with me but late that night, I couldn't stand it any longer. When G was asleep, I hauled myself out of bed and quietly got into the car.

It reminded me of the time I had sneaked out of Mr Raju's house to visit Zaheer's roadside grave.

I would be back before G even knew I was gone. As I was driving to the graveyard, I kept telling myself I was mad to do this but I had to see it tonight. This time it wasn't raining or thundering. It was a clear night.

By the time I got to the graveyard it was 11.30 p.m. It was locked. I nearly turned around and went back. 'I'll come back in the morning like a normal, sane person,' I told myself and started to walk away. 'But I'm here now and I really don't think I'll get any sleep till I see his grave.'

So I decided to try the gate. I rattled it and shook it but it was locked solid. I then decided to walk around the perimeter of the grounds. I cased the joint, looked for holes, for ways in but there were none. I was going to have to climb over the gate. It was an easy enough gate to climb but as I was six months pregnant and had stuffed my face with chocolate for the last four months like my life depended on it and had trouble climbing into bed at night, then climbing a gate was clearly going to be a challenge.

I huffed and puffed my way to the top of the gate. Trying to get over it was proving even more challenging than I'd thought. It was a miracle no one had spotted me, though the graveyard was set back in a secluded little cul de sac, so I felt quite sure no one would. The fact that I was going to a grave at nearly midnight should have been enough to scare me but I was determined.

I decided the best way to get over the gate was to support myself with my left leg in one of the diamonds in the grill of the gate and to swiftly swing my right leg over, hoping the momentum of the fling would catapult it over the top and I could then get a foothold on the other side. This I tried and it worked! There was only one slight problem. My trousers had got caught on one of the spikes on top of the gate; spikes put in specially for pregnant midnight grave trespassers like me.

I was stuck. It didn't matter how much I pulled or yanked at the trousers, they neither tore nor did they come loose. Damn Marks and Spencer! Why the bloody hell did they have to make their maternity pants so well? Couldn't they have made them from a flimsier material? Didn't they think to make a weak link in them in case a pregnant person needed to break free from them at some point?

Just as I was about to cry out of frustration, I heard a familiar voice.

"They say this is such a good graveyard, people are just *dying* to get in. You must be one of them."

Guillaume was standing at the foot of the gate with a bright torch which he shone in my face.

"How? But when…?" I tried to fathom how he came to be there.

Still shining the torch right in my face, he said calmly, "I heard you get up. I knew exactly where you were going, so I followed you. I thought you would see sense and turn around. You didn't. I knew you would need my help."

He then managed to climb over the gate and get to the other side and help me over. It was a small graveyard so not too difficult to find Heath's grave. The earth was still wet and unsettled. The gravestone lay beside it, ready to be placed once the mud had hardened. G shone the torch on the stone. We read it and wept in unison. For there on the gravestone were engraved the words: 'Born asleep to awake in heaven'.

Life on a Postcard No. 96
Coming Through Now

For a while, I didn't know whether Freya was avoiding me or I was avoiding her. When we spoke about this afterwards, she confessed she didn't feel the need to avoid me and I said I felt the same but it was almost like there was an unspoken rule that said, 'Those who hath had a miscarriage shall not associate, nor shall they cast eyes upon those who are with child'.

She thought I would prefer not to be reminded of what had happened, in case I worried it would happen to me and I thought the last thing she would want to see right in front of her, was a pregnant woman about to give birth.

Though I called her a few times and she made attempts to call me, we both knew it was out of politeness.

Not sure whether it was due to the stress and anxiety of what happened to Freya or the fact that I was now thumping around, like a large pregnant hippopotamus expecting triplets. I developed sciatica and was in agony most of the time as the nerve pressed down each time I walked. I couldn't sleep lying down anymore, got dreadful cramps and was crabby and irritable and just wanted her out of me already.

Then…

Three months after the dreadful event and a week before my due date, I had my final visit to the midwife. This time Mother insisted on coming as G was again on a shoot. I hoped it would be safe to take Mother on her own and was concerned that her conjoined twin might accompany her but I had made it very clear to Mum, that she had to come on her own. I didn't want them trying to tell the midwife what they thought she should do.

Once I was lying on the single bed with the crisp hard paper underneath me — a position I was now familiar with — she had a good feel around and scrunched up her face. *What now?* I thought.

"Your baby has engaged itself," she said.

So far so good, I thought.

"Its head's down," she said.

Good? I thought, clearly waiting for the 'but'.

"But" she said. (What did I tell you?)

"But," she repeated, interrupting my train of thought almost as if she could hear me thinking, "your baby is the wrong way around. It's spine to spine." Now I would like you to remember that phrase, as again it is possibly going to be more overused than my *miraculous* birth story.

"I suggest we book you in for a planned caesarean," she said.

"No," I said. "That's not going to happen," I explained. "This is my first and I am going to push it out come what may."

"You don't understand," the midwife emphasised. "A spine-to-spine birth is very painful. Many times more painful than a normal birth and a normal birth can be fairly painful, as those of us who have been through it know. It's very traumatic for the mother and for the baby as well and I would urge you to consider a planned caesarean."

"No way," I said again. "I've already booked my birthing pool, classical music and soothing aromatherapy oils."

"I really don't think you realise how painful it can be…" Her voice trailed off as she saw the determined look on my face.

"'Pah! How painful can it be?" I was beginning to sound like Freya.

For the next few days 'spine to spine' was echoed across the nation and other continents. It was looked up on the internet, discussed at dinners, lunches and I'm surprised the national grid didn't crash with the number of phone calls that went back and forth between all interested parties and even non-interested parties, such as Gayem, who was yet again dragged into the discussion against his will. Once again, advice came thick and fast.

By now, CA had got us all into conference calling as she wasn't able to get in touch with all of us at the same time when she needed information or wanted to dole out instructions.

Conference Call: 0900 hours T minus 96 hours and counting:

Mum: "Hot sweet tea. Drink lots of it that way the baby will turn around."

Hélène: "*Non*! *Mon dieu*! What are you talking about Vera? You need to drink pure, neat olive oil and the baby will just slip out."

CA: "Apparently, there is this amazing yogi in Harley Street who can give you some asanas to do, which will turn baby round to face the right way."

Gayem: "What? Why are you asking me again? I can't even imagine anything that big coming out of such a small hole, let alone facing the wrong way."

Adrian: "I will take you for a spin in my car and do a handbrake turn. If that doesn't turn the little thing, then nothing will."

Harry: "Let me take you for a round of football. That will

sort you out."

Nicole: "As usual, if you cannot come up with anything helpful, Harry, why the bloody hell do you bother?"

Harry: "Well, it's much more sensible than ridiculous things like drink tea, olive oil and standing on your head in a yoga pose."

Nicole: "No, it isn't, Harry. These are tried and tested methods and yours isn't. Now stop wasting our time. The best thing I think is, Charlotte, for you to have a really, nice, warm bath and relax…" (Actually, Nicole was beginning to make the most sense till…) "… with some lovely tea tree oil."

"NOOOOOO!' Everyone screamed! Essential oils are not recommended at all in pregnancies!"

Freya: "Just give me some gloves, some KY Jelly and I'll stick my hand in and turn the bally thing around myself. In fact, forget the bloody gloves!"

And finally, I had my Freya back

However, while it was great to hear her voice, Freya and I hadn't met since that day I left the hospital and I was desperate to see her.

1500 T minus 72 hours and counting.

I was out doing the last-minute shopping with Mother when I began to feel a few flutters and wondered whether that was the phantom signs they had told us about but brushed it aside.

1800 T minus 69 hours and counting

More flutters. Brushed aside again.

2200 T minus 66 hours and counting

The whole unruly bunch, including Adrian, Freya and Gayem, had come over for 'the Last Supper' as Father called it. He thought it was a great joke. Poor Dad had been quite out of it recently, as Mother and Hélène had taken over all things marriage and pregnancy. My walk was now a slow waddle, which I managed only by grabbing onto things as I went along. And along with all of them, also came Freya.

We were meeting for the first time in three months and we had a lot to catch up on. She had insisted on coming to the 'Last Supper' as she felt she needed to bite the bullet and see me before the birth. I wasn't sure she was ready for it and was reluctant to let her come but she could be very convincing and very few people said no to her.

She put on a brave face but I could see that this was affecting her even more than she thought it would. It wasn't something she could shrug off, as she had done all her life with anything that came her way. This was different. This was a baby. This was a life inside her. It was not the cancer lump she was delighted to have got rid of.

This she did not play on. This she did not joke about.

Just as we were finishing dinner, I needed to lie down so I waddled upstairs and just as my bottom was about to make contact with the bed, Mother came into the room to see if I was okay. At that very moment I let out a — I really cannot think of any other expression to use here — blood-curdling scream.

Mum said, "Okay, darling, I was just coming to check on you. There's no need to react that way."

"No Mum, as much as you do frustrate me sometimes, I'm not screaming as a result of you entering the room, I am screaming as a result of what I think is a baby trying to exit my womb."

Mum said, "What? Do you really think...? Oh, my goodness!" She rushed downstairs and then calmly asked G to pop upstairs and see how I was doing. She didn't want the whole horde upstairs.

He came up and I whispered through the agony of yet another contraction, "I think I'm in labour."

"Oh, my goodness! We need to get rid of that lot discreetly or they will all want to trail behind us in a convoy to the hospital."

He went downstairs, yawned casually and said, "*Alors, mes amis*, we are now quite tired so we are going to call it a night."

Unfortunately, and I have always said this, even if my life depended on it, G would not be able to lie with a straight face to save it.

Everyone else started to make gestures of getting ready to leave. Freya looked at G for a few seconds, then she let out a long, low whistle. Everyone stopped.

"Someone in this house is in labour" she said.

"No…" G tried to protest but now the mob mentality took over the guests and they wanted to know. G had to finally confess and tell them I was in labour but they had to leave as they would very soon either be an aunt, uncle, grandmother or grandfather.

Reluctantly, they all left apart from Mother. As planned, she and G would be with me at the birth.

Mum ushered them out quickly while G ran up to see if I was still okay and breathing. I was… just about. I told him I was in agony, we needed to go and not to forget the birthing bag, which for the last few days had been by the front door. He spent about ten minutes running around like a headless chicken trying to find the birthing bag. I asked him what he was looking for and he said, "The birthing bag of course! You think you would put it in an obvious…"

Yes, you guessed it; he found it in the most obvious place — by the front door, ready to go.

So off we went. It was at this point that Mother started to breathe more deeply than me, each time there was a contraction and at intervals of ten minutes she insisted on repeating, "I wish you'd agreed to have a caesarean. Then we wouldn't be going through this pain."

"Sorry? *We*?" I asked, irately. "*We* are going through this pain? Is there an eight-pound bundle trying to come out of your vagina at the moment? No? Then *we* are not in pain, Mother, *I* am!"

Life on a Postcard No. 97
Can It Get Any More Complicated?

Finally, I was in the hospital.

I was in a room but in absolute agony, huffing, puffing, panting and doing anything I could to stop myself screaming. Mother was wringing her hands. I wondered whether mothers had learnt somewhere that that helped. I wondered whether when I became a mother, handwringing would come automatically to me. As I was lying there looking at G — calm, reassuring, smiling down on me, in no pain — I wanted to grab the nearest sharp object and plunge it into his chest. That urge soon faded and I looked at him, this sweet man, this adorable, gorgeous Frenchman, trying to calm my hand-wringing mother down and then running to me each time he heard a groan and asking me to 'Breathe', putting good use to all the learning he'd gained from the antenatal classes and all my primal urges to plunge something sharp into his chest dissipated and I now wanted to wring his neck with my bare hands.

Thankfully, just as I was reaching for his jugular, the nurse walked in with a cheery, "Hello!" which almost tinkled as she said it.

"How are we doing?" she chirped, with a trill.

"We are doing spiffingly," I said, through gritted teeth.

"Come, come now," she said. "This is all part of giving birth. We can't get the little bundle of joy out without a bit of push and pull now, can we?"

I now had someone else I could turn my homicidal attention onto. Unfortunately, she didn't get close enough and as strong as my urge was to see her die a painful death, I couldn't overcome the pain.

I just about managed to squeeze out, "Pain… Spine to spine… Midwife said caesarean."

"Yes, well, it's too late for that now, isn't it?" she bubbled away. "How about we follow your birth plan that you laid out for yourself? Let me see now: no drugs at all, birthing pool…"

As she started to read out my sheet, I wanted to shout out, 'No, forget the fucking birth plan! Forget what I said. Just give me all the drugs you have; all drugs known and unknown and if you have some that you are trialling, I will have those as well'.

Just as I was about to say that I had another contraction and G was by my side saying, "Breathe, breathe. Pant, pant. This one's nearly over, my darling. Just a few seconds longer."

As soon as that had passed and I was about to go back to begging for the drugs again, Nursie twittled again. "Now you asked for the birthing pool. Let's pop you in there for a bit and see how that goes."

Before I knew it, she and G had put me in a wheelchair and were taking me into a room that I must admit was very large, echoey but strangely calming. The water was warm and it really did help being in there.

Mother asked the nurse if it was safe and what if the baby came out and drowned. "Ha, Ha, Ha!" Nursie chortled. "That isn't going to happen, Mrs Baxter and it's going to be a *long* time before baby comes, so settle down as we are in for a long night. I will be back in a bit with doctor."

I knew that as soon as I was able, she would be the

absolute first on my hit list. If I couldn't kill her for legal reasons, at least I was going to maim her. And don't you just hate it when nurses say 'doctor' instead of calling them by their name? It's like they are talking to a three-year-old out of a Ladybird Book.

No sooner had she left, when the shock on my face brought G running over again from attending to Mother, who was wondering at what point they both needed to get in the pool with me and how would that work.

"What is it, my darling?" he said, "another contraction?" I started to puff and pant. He said, "Breathe. Breathe." Still panting, I shook my head and pointed to the window of the birthing-pool room.

Through the window, a bottom emerged, followed by a body and then I saw a hand push the head through the window — it was Gayem swiftly followed by Freya.

"For goodness sake, stop panicking, DK," she said. "We're in now."

I was still panting and pointing, unable to believe what I was seeing. G and Mother were speechless. Freya surveyed her surroundings. "Well, this will have to do, I guess," she said.

Then she turned her attention to me, "Right, now let's get this baby out."

G was incandescent with rage. "Freya, Gayem, you *cannot* be here. The nurse will be back any minute. This is crazy. This is the one time you really need to leave us alone."

Gayem started to speak. "I told Frey we absolutely must *not* come. She forced me. She gave me a Chinese burn and said she would hurt me if…"

Freya put her hand up to his face and turned to G. "I am

minus one breast and…" That's where she stopped, as even she could not bring herself to say it but she continued. "I know this is your special moment and we will leave as soon as we have got her through the worst bit. Would you deny me the pleasure of that after what I have been through?" That was as close as she could refer to her miscarriage and that's when I knew it had hit her hard.

G couldn't argue with that very much. He said they could stay just for a few minutes.

Freya had a plan. She wanted Gayem to get in one side and support my legs and she would support my back and G would support my shoulders and could do the 'breathe, breathe' part. She had it all planned and then she took off her clothes under which she had her swimming costume. I had to admire her for this level of planning.

Gayem looked at her and she said, "Please tell me you have trunks under there."

"Of course not!" Gayem said.

"I did tell you to wear them. Why didn't you?" Freya admonished him.

Gayem now said, "There is no way I am getting into that pool with all the stuff that might come out and I am certainly not going on the *nu-nu* side." Freya looked at him in disgust.

"Where the hell did you come up with a name like that for a vagina?"

"Well, it all started when some of the queens got together at college and we were having a few drinks, when we started to talk about whether we had ever had sex with a woman and whether any of us could do the vagina thing. And we all said, "noooo, nooooo". Hence it became known as the *nu-nu*."

"Really? Seriously guys," I interjected, "you're having

this conversation right now? I am homicidal! Do you know what that means? I want to kill someone, anyone and you are talking about how you coined the word *nu-nu*? Give me a fucking break!"

"Okay, you're right," said Freya. "Let's get in, DK."

"I am not getting in," Gayem said.

"Just get your trousers off and get in in your boxers," Freya suggested.

"No way," he said.

Freya started to pull his trousers off and he resisted. G went over to try and stop her and they started arguing. Freya slipped and started to fall into the pool, pulling Gayem in with her, who was holding onto G for dear life and dragged him in on top of him.

Mother's hand-wringing reached a crescendo and she finally gave up and started using her voice instead.

"'Get out of there, you complete idiots!'" she shouted. She had had enough and turned her anger towards me as well. "If you had just listened to the midwife and gone with the planned caesarean none of this would have happened and you wouldn't be in this kind of pain."

Just as she was about to launch at the others, in walked 'Nursie' with 'Doctor' and I doubt in all their lives as medical students, residents or professionals, they had ever met the sight they were looking at now.

I was going through another contraction, G was still grappling with Gayem trying to get him out of the pool, while shouting to me, "Breathe, breathe," Freya was still trying to get round to holding my back and Mother was shouting at all of us from the edge of the pool, her voice echoing round the room like a synthesiser set on repeat

Nurse puffed herself up like a rooster who was about to explode and I almost expected a high pitched 'Cock-a-doodle-do' to come out, but instead she huffed in a loud voice with a low tone, "What is the meaning of this?"

'Doctor' (clearly from the Freya school of communication) put his hand up to Nursies' face and said, "Could someone please explain the meaning of this?"

G, Gayem and Freya all started to speak at once, pleading their case as to why they were in the pool with me. The doctor again put his hand up, palm facing towards all of them. They stopped in an instance but Freya had her mouth slightly open. She was normally the palm-gesture person, not the one to whom the palm gesture was done. This was a new position for her.

Doctor said slowly, "Who is the father?"

There was no answer from any of them as I think they were still trying to think of how they were going to plead their case. When he didn't get an answer, the doctor said, "Well, I suppose in this day and age, I do need to be politically correct and perhaps ask, who is going to help bring up the child?"

"We all are," came back the answer, in chorus.

G decided he would straighten things out. "I'm the father," he said in his best Darth Vadar voice, "and these friends of ours are just leaving."

Freya was not about to give up without a fight. "You see, doctor," she started, "I have been through a mastectomy and…"

"I am sorry about that, Madam," the doctor stopped her halfway through her sentence, "but right now my concern is for this little one to be delivered as smoothly as possible and the last time we had this many people in the pool, was when they were building it, so can you all please get out, dry off and leave quietly?"

Freya and Gayem got out, glum and sheepish and dripped their way out of the room. G got out and dried himself and got into his proper attire to support me.

The doctor read my notes and said, "We need her on a bed."

I was then transported back to my room, dried off and given gas and air which I gratefully received.

Mother was happy we were back out of that silly pool and somewhere a bit more stable and 'normal'. I had now been in labour for ten hours and was already seven centimetres dilated. She was just about to ask G if he wanted a nice cup of tea when 'doctor' stuck me on a monitor. As soon as he did so, he and 'nursie' exchanged a glance; nursie said quickly, "'I'll call for the bed to transport her."

Doctor said, "No time for that. We're just going to have to wheel her on this ourselves."

Mother had just turned around to get her purse to go for her cuppa and G was still jumping on one leg, trying to get some water out of one ear, when one minute I was there and the next minute I was being whisked away by Doctor and Nursie.

As Mother and G started to run behind the bed and nursie called out, "Don't worry. She'll be fine. We just need to get baby out. No oxygen going to the brain. Back in a spot!"

Poor Mother and G were left standing in the middle of a wide, quiet corridor with no one to ask for an explanation. From my point of view, I was sucking on the gas and air so much that I was quite out of it. There was no time for an epidural apparently and they explained to me as they went along.

"We're not sure what has happened but there is no oxygen going to the baby's brain. We need to get her out as soon as possible and have to give you a crash caesarean. Don't worry, we have it in hand."

"Really?" is all I remember saying.

Mother and G waited patiently for what felt like forever. Finally, they saw nursie rushing towards them with a tiny bundle wrapped in a towel.

"It was scary in there for a few moments but all is well now," she chirped, as she approached them. "Look at this. Isn't it amazing?"

With that, she handed G and Mother the bundle. They opened it up and there in their hands was an umbilical cord with a huge knot in it.

"It's called a true knot," Nursie enthused. She was marvelling at it as one might actually marvel at a newborn. "It's very unusual and baby must have looped around herself sometime during the birth and tied a knot in her own cord. When baby was in Mummy's tummy all was well, as there was no tension on the cord but as baby started to come down through the birth canal, the knot got tighter and tighter, hence no oxygen to the brain. But we managed to catch it in time and though it was touch and go, it was a miracle we managed to get baby out before any damage took place."

At that word, Mother and G looked at each other and burst into fits of laughter and tears all at the same time. The relief and irony of this birth did not pass by them.

Soon Lilya Rose was placed into G's shaking hands and Mother was given the tiniest bottle to feed her with.

Life on a Postcard No. 98
When A Child Is Born, So Is A Mother

I could hear voices. I blinked a few times but couldn't quite keep my eyes open. I closed them again. I can only assume much later I heard a baby crying. I could barely see but I strained my neck and saw Nicole holding her. I gently stroked her cheek and said, "Don't cry," then fell back to sleep. The crying stopped.

The next thing I remember was the doctor trying to rouse me, to make sure I was out of the anaesthetic. "Are you okay, my dear? Can you hear me? I need to make sure you're conscious before I leave here. It was touch-and-go, you know? We had to act quickly. I don't think you realise how close we were to losing her. We had to give you a crash caesarean. There was not time to do anything else."

The only thing I could get out at this time was, "Oh no! Does that mean you saw my nu-nu?"

Nicole and Doctor exchanged a glance, as neither of them knew what that was. The doctor reassured Nicole it was the drugs talking.

I vaguely remember Mother and G being there and hearing Harry in the background, then there was a scuffle and shuffle and Lilya Rose was placed next to me and G took about one hundred frames per second and then she was taken off me again and I fell asleep.

As I slowly came to, I began to realise something was strange about this picture. What was Nicole doing here and where was everyone else? When I was able to, I asked her.

"Your mum and G have gone to get some refreshments," she said. "They've been up all night with you and they need to rest. I came as soon as I knew she'd been born."

"How long have you been here?" I asked.

"Three hours," she said.

"And how long have you been cradling her in your arms?" I asked.

"Three hours," she said.

"You don't have to keep holding her, you know," I said.

"I know," she said.

I took her slowly from Nicole and held her in my arms. As I did so, I saw G walking towards me. He sat on the bed next to me. I snuggled close to him. There in my arms was the most gorgeous, most amazing creature I had ever seen. Stoooooop! No baby who has just been born, especially spine to spine where they have been crushed and pushed and squeezed down the birth canal, up to seven-centimetre dilation, could be the most amazing creature. She was scrunched-up, patchy and pink but she wasn't what you would call ugly. This was a huge relief to me.

What I will say is this: she was the most amazing thing I had done in my life.

I had hang-glided off the Corcovado Mountain and soared up to the statue of Jesus Christ, circled it once and wanted to confess all my sins, visited heaven on earth, swum with wild dolphins in the middle of the Atlantic Ocean, delivered a baby at thirty-five thousand feet, slapped a defibrillator on a fifty-year-old woman during heavy turbulence, while giving her CPR and saving her life, handcuffed a violent passenger with a broken nose (my nose, not his!), rammed an adrenaline